Table of Contents

Sunday Savers™ Activities to Make Learning Fun for Primary 5 – D&C/Church History

Table of Contents #1 (1-46 Lesson Subjects & Activities)...................... i-ii

Table of Contents #2 (Preview of A-Z Gospel Subjects & Activities)............. iii-vi

Sunday Savers Introduction with My Gospel Activity Notebook Cover............. vii-x

Lessons 1-46 Activities.. 1-91

Scripture Challenge Cards to Match Lessons 1-46............................. 92-115

TABLE OF CONTENTS #1 (1-46 Lesson Subjects & Activities to Match Primary 5 Manual)

#	Lesson	Activity	Pages
1	Joseph Smith's First Vision	Testimony Bookmark	1-2
2	Apostasy and Restoration of Jesus' Church	Apostasy Mirror-puzzle	3-5
3	Gospel Fullness Good News Message	Angel Moroni's Match Game	6-8
4	Prepare to Serve Jesus and Others	Prepare or Beware! Maze	6, 9
5	Heavenly Father Will Help Me As I Obey	Message Dangler	10-11
6	Seeking Guidance Through Prayer	Prayer Crossword Puzzle	12-13
7	The Holy Ghost Will Guide & Comfort Me	Invite the Spirit Game	12, 14-15
8	Being Worthy of Priesthood Blessings	Priesthood Power! Word Search	16-17
9	Testimony of Truth & the Book of Mormon	Slide-show/Doorknob Hanger	16, 18-19
10	Grateful for the Book of Mormon	Typesetting Poster	20-22
11	The True Church Was Restored to the Earth	Then-and-Now Match Game	23-24
12	Grateful to Be Baptized	Ordinance Opportunity Game	25-27
13	Sharing the Gospel of Jesus Christ	Bendable Missionary Dolls	28-30
14	Sacred Hymns Bring Blessings	"Note"able Hymns Secret Code Message	28, 31
15	The Prophet Speaks and I Listen	Revelation Routes	32-33
16	Love and Unity Help Others	Woven Heart Message	32, 34
17	Supporting Church Leaders	Bishop Bingo	35-39
18	Building Up the Kingdom of God	Law of Consecration Checkbook	40-41

19	Recognizing True Gifts of the Spirit	Gifts Match Game	40, 42
20	Love to Study the Scriptures	Scattered Scriptures Mix-n-Match	43-46
21	Forgiving Others and Finding Peace	Bite-size Memorize	43, 47
22	Prophets Giving Revelation	Standard-Works Thinkathon Game	48-50
23	Celestial Life with Heavenly Father and Jesus	Connected Kingdoms	51-53
24	Say "No" to Harmful and "Yes" to Healthful	Word of Wisdom Voting Ballot	54-55
25	We Are Blessed When We Sacrifice	Giving Oyster Mirror Motivator	54, 56
26	Unlock the Powers of Heaven	Priesthood Keys Door Reminder	57-58
27	We Are Blessed as We Obey	BLACKOUT! Promise Puzzle	57, 59
28	Trials Strengthen Faith	Premortal Life/Earth Life Quiz	60-61
29	Share the Gospel of Jesus Christ	Missionary-Stretch Chart	60, 62-63
30	Prepare to Meet Jesus at Second Coming	Strong Heart Mobile	64-65
31	Prophet Guides as We Listen	Choices-and-Consequences Crossmatch	64, 66
32	Faithfully Rely on Heavenly Father	Bite-size Memorize	67-68
33	Work & Leave a Legacy of Love	Pioneer Spirit Thank-you Card	67, 69
34	Baptisms for the Dead	Tracing My Ancestors Pedigree Chart	70-72
35	Live Worthy for Temple Blessings	Temple Photo Frame	70, 73
36	Articles of Faith Strengthen Testimony	13 Lucky Numbers Game	74-75
37	Prophet Joseph Smith Restored Jesus' Gospel	Tribute Search	76-77
38	The Prophet Today Leads Us	Zion or Bust! Handcart Checklist	76, 78
39	Service Brings Happiness	Service-station Sack of Reminders	79-80
40	Work Hard to Serve Like the Pioneers	Pioneer Word-find Puzzle	79, 81
41	Keep the Sabbath Day Holy	Sabbath-day Decisions Drama-or-draw	82-84
42	Faith in Jesus Christ Helps Me	"Jesus Lights up My Life" Light-switch Cover	82, 85
43	Valiantly Live the Gospel of Jesus Christ	Valiant Poster	86-87
44	Living the Law of Chastity	Temple-light Poster	86, 88
45	Tithing Helps Build Up the Kingdom of God	Origami Tithing Purse/Wallet	89-90
46	Study and Prayer Strengthen Testimony	Testimony Word Race	89, 91
Scripture Challenge Cards to Match Lessons 1-46		With Glue-on Motivation Stickers	92-115

Sunday Savers™

Doctrine and Covenants/Church History—Ages 8-11

ACTIVITIES, THOUGHT TREATS, &

SCRIPTURE CHALLENGE CARDS

to correlate with the Primary 5 D&C/Church History manual lessons

USE FOR PRIMARY
LESSONS AND
FAMILY HOME
EVENING
TO ENHANCE
LEARNING

THE BOOK OF MORMON: ANOTHER TESTAMENT OF JESUS CHRIST.

First Vision

3 Nephi 11:10
"Behold, I am Jesus Christ whom the prophets testified shall come into the world."

My Scripture Challenge Cards

Book Belongs to:

Introducing the Author and Illustrator, Creators of the Following Books and Printable CD-ROM Versions of Each Book

- **Primary Lesson Activities & Handouts (for manuals 1-7 & Activity Days):** Look for the following Sunday Savers or Primary Partners books for: Nursery vol. 1-2, Happy Handouts (vol. 3), CTR-A, CTR-B, Book of Mormon, D&C, New Testament, Old Testament, We Love Activity Days, and Super Activity Days and Socials

- **Current Year's Sharing Time:** Sunday Savers: Sharing Fun (12 activities), Sharing Fun Treasures (30-50 activities), Singing Fun (visuals for practice songs), Children's Song Sing Along Video

- **Games and Activities for Family Home Evening & Primary:** CD-ROMs and color books with pages that are ready to tear out and use: Gospel Fun Activities, Fun in a Flash, Tons of Fun, Jesus Loves Me, Gospel Games, Funner Than Fun Gospel Games, Short & Sweet with a Treat: 52 Already Done, Ready-for-Fun Family Home Evenings (CD-ROM included!)

- **Young Women:** Young Women Fun-tastic! Activities: Lesson Lifesavers for manuals 1-3 and Young Women Fun-tastic! Personal Progress Motivators

MARY ROSS, author, is the wife of Paul Ross and mother of Jennifer. They live in Lehi, Utah. She has been a Primary teacher, Relief Society president, and self-image instructor. She has studied acting, voice, modeling, and cooking. She enjoys giving parties and writing.

JENNETTE GUYMON-KING, illustrator is the wife of Clayton King and mother of Kayla, Shelby, Levi, and Carson. They live in Bluffdale, Utah. She has studied graphic arts, served a mission in Japan, enjoys sports, reading, cooking, art, gardening, and freelance illustrating.

Copyright © 2009 by Mary H. Ross and Jennette Guymon-King
All Rights Reserved

Covenant Communications, Inc., American Fork, Utah

Printed in the United States of America

First Printing: January 1997

Sunday Savers: Doctrine & Covenants, Ages 8-11

ISBN 10: 1-5981-743-2

ISBN 13: 978-1-59811-743-1

ACKNOWLEDGMENTS: Thanks to Inspire Graphics (www.inspiregraphics.com) for the use of Lettering Delights computer fonts for some activities.

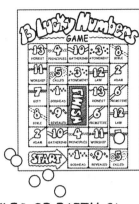

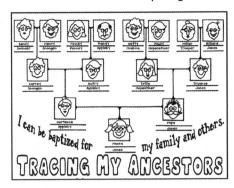

2—APOSTASY: Jesus' Church Is Restored (Apostasy Mirror), 3-5

36—ARTICLES OF FAITH Strengthen Testimony (13 Lucky Numbers), 74-75

34—BAPTISM FOR DEAD: Tracing Ancestors (Pedigree Chart), 70-72

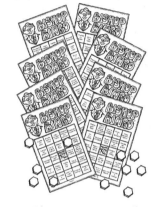

17—BISHOPS: Supporting Church Leaders (Bishop Bingo), 35-39

9—BOOK OF MORMON: Testimony of Truth (Doorknob Slide-show), 16, 18-19

10—BOOK OF MORMON: Grateful for Book (Typesetting Poster), 20-22

23—CELESTIAL: Life with Heavenly Father/Jesus (Connected Kingdoms), 51-53

27—COMMANDMENTS: Obedience Blessings (BLACKOUT Puzzle), 57, 59

42—FAITH in Jesus Christ Helps Me (Light-Switch Cover), 82, 85

32—FAITH: Relying on Heavenly Father (Bite-size Memorize), 67-68

1—FIRST VISION: Joseph Smith's Vision (Testimony Bookmark), 1-2

21—FORGIVENESS: Forgiving and Finding Peace (Bite-size Memorize), 43, 47

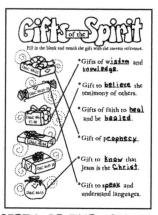

19—GIFTS OF THE SPIRIT:
Recognizing Gifts (Match Game), 40, 42

3—GOSPEL FULNESS: Good News
(Angel Moroni's Match Game), 6-8

7—HOLY GHOST: Guide & Comfort
(Invite the Spirit Game), 12, 14-15

14—HYMNS Bless Us ("Note"able
Hymns Secret Code Message), 28, 31

18—LAW OF CONSECRATION:
Build Up Kingdom (Checkbook), 40-41

16—LOVE & UNITY Help Others
(Woven Heart Message), 32, 34

13—MISSIONARY: Share Gospel
(Bendable Missionary Dolls), 28-30

29—MISSIONARY: Share Gospel
(Missionary Stretch Chart), 60, 62-63

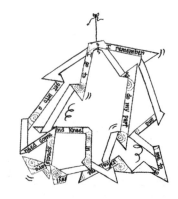

5—OBEDIENCE: Heavenly Father
Helps Me (Message Dangler), p. 10-11

12—ORDINANCES: Baptism Gratitude
(Ordinance Opportunity Game), 25-27

40—PIONEERS: Work Hard to Serve
(Pioneer Word-find Puzzle), 79, 81

33—PIONEER SPIRIT: Work & Leave
Legacy (Thank-you Card), 67, 69

6—PRAYER: Seeking Guidance (Prayer Crossword Puzzle), 12-13

4—PREPARE: Serving Jesus and Others (Prepare or Beware! Maze), 6, 9

8—PRIESTHOOD BLESSINGS: Priesthood Power! Word Search), 16-17

26—PRIESTHOOD KEYS: Unlock Powers of Heaven (Reminder), 57-58

31—PROPHET GUIDES: Listen and Obey (Crossmatch), 64, 66

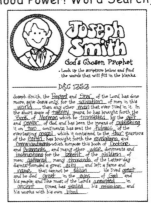

37—PROPHET JOSEPH SMITH: (Scripture Search), 76-77

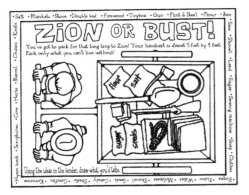

38—PROPHET OF TODAY: Lead Us (Zion or Bust! Handcard Check), 76, 78

11—RESTORATION: True Church Restored (Then-and-Now Match), 23-24

15—REVELATION: Prophet Speaks (Revelation Routes), 32-33

22—REVELATION From Prophets (Standard Works Thinkathon), 48-40

41—SABBATH DAY: Keep Holy (Decisions Drama-or-draw), 82-84

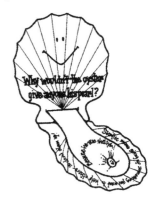

25—SACRIFICE: Blessed When We Sacrifice (Giving Oyster Mirror Motivator), 54, 56

20—SCRIPTURES: Love to Study (Mix-n-Match), 43-46

30—SECOND COMING: Prepare to Meet Jesus (Strong Heart Mobile), 64-65

39—SERVICE Brings Happiness (Service-station Sack of Reminders), 79-80

44—TEMPLE MARRIAGE: Law of Chastity (Temple-light Poster), 86, 88

35—TEMPLES: Live Worthy (Temple Photo Frame), 70, 73

46—TESTIMONY: Study & Prayer Strengthen Testimony (Word Race), 89, 91

45—TITHING: Build up Kingdom (Origami Tithing Purse), 89-90

28—TRIALS STRENGTHEN FAITH: (Premortal Life/Earth Life Quiz), 60-61

43—VALIANT: Valiantly Live Gospel of Jesus Chrsit (Valiant Poster), 86-87

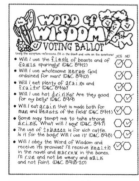

24—WORD OF WISDOM: Say "No" to Harmful and "Yes" to Healthful (Word of Wisdom Voting Ballot), 54-55

Introduction

Sunday Savers™ Doctrine and Covenants and Church History, ages 8-11 contains visuals, crafts, games, handouts, and activities that match every lesson in the Primary 5 D&C/Church History manual.

Simply find the lesson in the manual or on the Internet at lds.org. Then copy the visuals in this book, or print them from the CD-ROM in color or black-and-white (sold separately, shown right and on the back cover of this book).

Sunday Savers (formerly called Primary Partners) are sure to add to and enhance each lesson. Since "a picture is worth a 1,000 words," use these visuals to help children get the most out of lessons in both family home evening and Primary.

HOW TO USE THIS BOOK

TABLE OF CONTENTS: Use to find lesson match activities for week-to-week lessons 1-46 or use the A-Z contents to spot gospel subjects quickly.

SHARE MATCHING ACTIVITIES: These activities correlate with specific parts of the lesson. See the PREPARATION section for each lesson. When there is time after the lesson, you'll have something fun to do, or you can use the activity visuals to help you teach the lesson concepts. E.g., for the "First Vision" testimony bookmark activity (shown left) compliments the D&C/Church History Lesson 1 enrichment activities suggested on page 4 in the Primary 5 manual.

With the wide variety of activities in this book, there will never be a dull moment in Primary or family home evening. For example, with the Invites the Spirit Game

(shown right) for Lesson 7, children can learn about choices that invite the Holy Ghost or turn the Spirit away.

CHALLENGE SCRIPTURE STUDY: Help children learn by giving them a SCRIPTURE CHALLENGE card (shown right) each week. Each card correlates with the Suggested Home Reading scripture at the end of each lesson in the manual. You will find these on p. 92-115. Children can enclose these cards in an envelope or make a book by punching the two holes on the left of card and inserting them behind the two front cover pages. Tie a string or shoelace through holes with the bow in the back (long enough so children can keep inserting pages week after week. Children can fill in the blanks and color the image to indicate their testimony is growing.

#1   First Vision:
Joseph Smith Saw Heavenly Father and Jesus

Search & Ponder Challenge:
Read Joseph Smith—History 1:1-20

Joseph Smith—History 1:18-19
"No sooner, therefore, did I get possession of myself, so as to be able to speak, than I asked the Personages who ___ ___ ___ ___ ___ above me in the light, which of all the sects was ___ ___ ___ ___ ___ (for . . . it had never entered into my heart that ___ ___ ___ were wrong)--and which I should join. I was answered that I must join ___ ___ ___ ___ ___ of them."

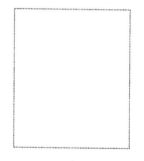

My Gospel Activity
NOTEBOOK
I'm Trying to Be Like Jesus

Picture of Me at Age ___

I Will Search, Ponder, and Pray,
and Try to Be More Like Jesus Each Day.

I Will Read the Scriptures Daily

Articles of Faith Memorization Checklist:

1 ___ 2 ___ 3 ___ 4 ___ 5 ___ 6 ___ 7 ___

8 ___ 9 ___ 10 ___ 11 ___ 12 ___ 13 ___

THOUGHT TREATS: These treats can be used to match lesson subjects when appropriate.

CREATE A JOURNAL OR NOTEBOOK: This can be done by copying the cover page (shown left) that follows and inserting it into a binder. Then children can insert handouts into the binder. They can add their photo and age for the year. Then, as they memorize the 13 Articles of Faith, they can check the space provided on the notebook cover.

COPY LESSON ACTIVITIES: Make copies ahead of time and gather supplies to avoid last-minute preparation. Look for the supplies needed in the TO MAKE section for each activity. Supplies: scissors, tape, glue, markers, plastic bags, lunch-size sack, paper punch, yarn or ribbon, and paper fasteners.

SCRIPTURE CHALLENGE CARDS:

Encourage children to look up the scriptures on the
cards, fill in the missing words, and color the image. Tell
them that as they do this, their testimony will grow.
All cards can also be printed from the CD-ROM for this book
(sold separately).

TWO WAYS TO STORE

SCRIPTURE CHALLENGE CARDS (found on p. 92-115).

Option #1 CREATE A SCRIPTURE CHALLENGE BOOK:

Have children place all cards in a book at the beginning
of the year or add to the book week by week. The
example (shown right) shows the book option.

    To make book, cut out all cards. Punch two holes
on left of cards and two holes on the front cover
(p. 92). Thread a shoelace or string through holes,
placing the cover on top. If giving cards to children
week by week, tie bow in back.

Option #2 CREATE A SCRIPTURE CHALLENGE ENVELOPE:

With this option, children can insert cards in an envelope. All
46 cards can slide into envelope easily. The envelope makes it
easy for children to take cards out to read and work on. Leave
the hole punch area on the side of cards in case children
decide to place them in a book later (using Option #1 above).
Label (p. 92) can be mounted on front and back of envelope.

Two Ways to Create Envelope:

1. LETTER-SIZED ENVELOPE: Fold the flap of a letter-sized
envelope back 1/4" to make room for cards.

2. MAKE TWO ENVELOPES FROM ONE LARGE ENVELOPE:

Seal the open end of a 9" x 12" envelope. Then fold in half and cut on crease to form two 6" x 9"
pockets. At the opening of each, cut a 1½" slit down both sides. Fold one flap in and the other out.

My Gospel Activity NOTEBOOK
I'm Trying to Be Like Jesus

Picture of Me at Age __

I Will Search, Ponder, and Pray,
and Try to Be More Like Jesus Each Day.

I Will Read the Scriptures Daily

Articles of Faith Memorization Checklist:

1 __ 2 __ 3 __ 4 __ 5 __ 6 __ 7 __

8 __ 9 __ 10 __ 11 __ 12 __ 13 __

Lesson 1	Joseph Smith's First Vision

PREPARATION: Review Lesson 1 and enrichment activities 4 and 6 (p. 4) in the Primary 5 D&C/Church History manual.

ACTIVITY:
Testimony Bookmark

Help children memorize Joseph Smith's testimony of the truth of what he discovered as he knelt in the Sacred Grove. Have children place bookmark in their scriptures to remind them to have faith like the Prophet Joseph Smith.

TO MAKE: Copy, color, and cut out the bookmark that follows for each child on cardstock paper. Fold it in half and glue back-to-back. Laminate. Paper-punch a hole at top and tie a six-inch ribbon through and tie a knot.

SCRIPTURE CHALLENGE: See p. 92, 93

THOUGHT TREAT (when appropriate):
Sacred Grove Cone Cakes.
1. Pour cake batter into ice cream cone (flat on bottom) until half full.
2. Bake in 350° oven 20–22 minutes.
3. Frost cupcake cones with green frosting.
4. Tell children that the green-topped cones (when placed together) look like the grove of trees where Joseph Smith knelt when he saw Heavenly Father and Jesus Christ. The children can also receive a testimony of the First Vision as they pray to Heavenly Father.
5. Read James 1:5 and tell children that this is the scripture Joseph Smith read in the Bible that encouraged him to pray to know the truth.

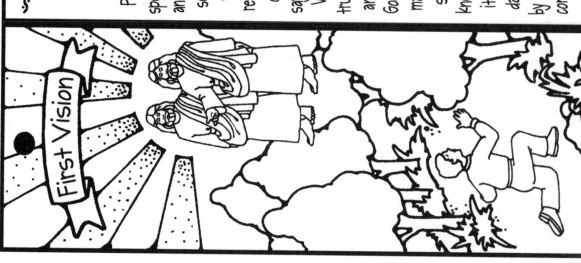

First Vision

"So it was with me, I had actually seen a light, and in the midst of that light I saw two Personages, and they did in reality speak to me; and though I was hated and persecuted for saying that I had seen a vision, yet it was true; and while they were persecuting me, reviling me, and speaking all manner of evil against me falsely for so saying, I was led to say in my heart: Why persecute me for telling the truth? I have actually seen a vision; and who am I that I can withstand God, or why does the world think to make me deny what I have actually seen? For I had seen a vision; I knew it, and I knew that God knew it, and I could not deny it, neither dared I do it; at least I knew that by so doing I would offend God, and come under condemnation."

—Joseph Smith History 1:25

First Vision

"So it was with me, I had actually seen a light, and in the midst of that light I saw two Personages, and they did in reality speak to me; and though I was hated and persecuted for saying that I had seen a vision, yet it was true; and while they were persecuting me, reviling me, and speaking all manner of evil against me falsely for so saying, I was led to say in my heart: Why persecute me for telling the truth? I have actually seen a vision; and who am I that I can withstand God, or why does the world think to make me deny what I have actually seen? For I had seen a vision; I knew it, and I knew that God knew it, and I could not deny it, neither dared I do it; at least I knew that by so doing I would offend God, and come under condemnation."

—Joseph Smith History 1:25

Lesson 2   Apostasy & Restoration of Jesus' Church

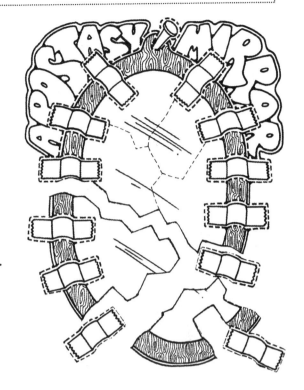

PREPARATION: Review Lesson 2 scriptural and historical accounts (page 8-9) and suggested family sharing (page 11) in the Primary 5 D&C/Church History manual.

ACTIVITY:
Apostasy Mirror-puzzle

Children can use this as a tool to teach their families about the Apostasy and Restoration of the Church of Jesus Christ as they put up and take down the puzzle. Children can read the Apostasy Mirror concept page to explain.

TO MAKE: Copy, color, and cut out the visuals that follow for each child on cardstock paper. Place label inside plastic bag with puzzle pieces to help children teach their family and friends. Have children fold the Apostasy Mirror concept page in half (with mirror on the other side of visual) to place in their scriptures as a reminder.

SCRIPTURE CHALLENGE: See p. 92, 93

THOUGHT TREAT (when appropriate): Apostasy Cookie Crumble. Give children a sandwich-type cookie filled with frosting that they can take apart (e.g., Oreo-type cookie). Talk about the apostasy, using Option 1 or Option 2 as follows.

Option 1: Say, "Jesus organized the Church of Jesus Christ when He was on the earth. After He and His 12 apostles died, the truth crumbled (separate cookie into two parts and crumble one cookie half). Christ's teachings broke away into many different beliefs. Then Joseph Smith prayed to find the true church. Because he asked Heavenly Father for the truth, The Church of Jesus Christ of Latter-day Saints was restored." (Take a good half of another cookie and place it on top of the frosting to make a complete sandwich cookie.)

Option 2: Review the 8th Article of Faith. Then say, "The Bible is one testament of Jesus Christ (show one side of cookie), and the Book of Mormon is another testament of Jesus Christ (show other side of cookie). We can study the Bible and Book of Mormon and pray to know of the truths they hold. Our prayers help us gain a firm testimony that helps us keep the commandments, like the frosting that holds these two cookies together. As we search, ponder, and pray about the scriptures, we can gain a firm testimony that the Church of Jesus Christ was restored in these latter days."

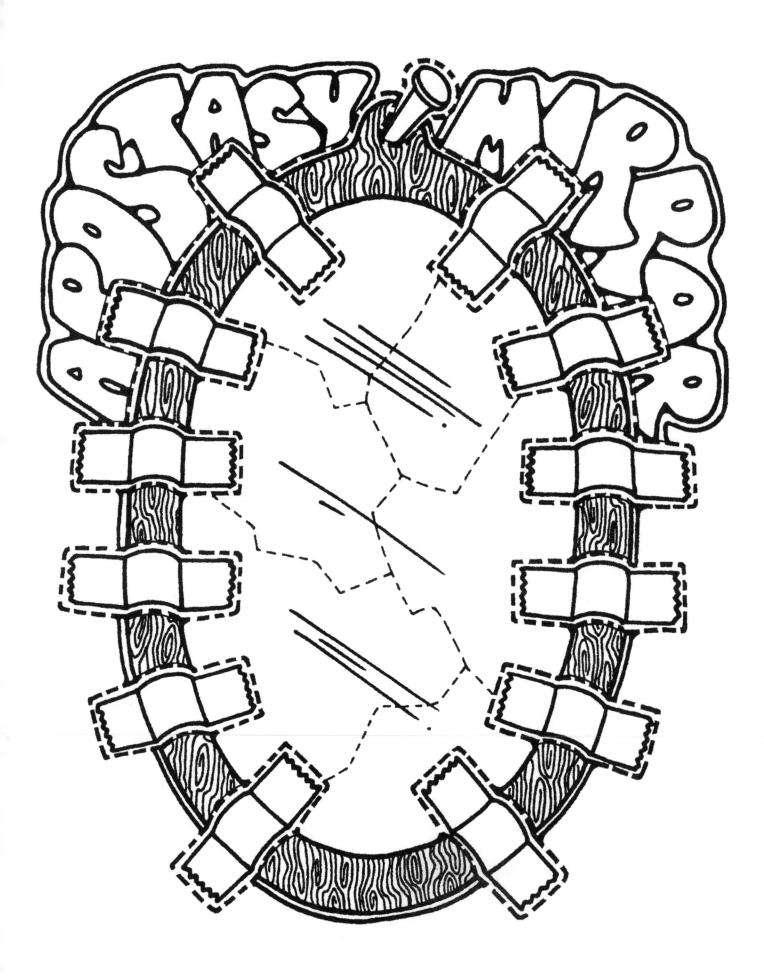

Apostasy Mirror

The Apostasy Mirror

This mirror represents the Church of Jesus Christ. The mirror represents the Church itself, with Christ at the top as the nail, and each of the Apostles as a piece of tape. When Christ died, the Apostles held up the mirror and took care of the affairs of the Church. When the Apostles were killed, the mirror fell and broke, thus resulting in the Apostasy. But people still saw good in the mirror and took pieces and built around them, resulting in the many churches of today. This exemplifies the reason we needed a Restoration and not just a reformation . . . because a mirror that has been broken cannot be repaired — it must be replaced.

Lesson 3 — Gospel Fullness Good News Message

PREPARATION: Review Lesson 3 and enrichment activity 3 (p. 14) in the Primary 5 D&C/Church History manual.

ACTIVITY: Angel Moroni's Match Game

This game reminds children of the basic elements of the gospel that were restored to Joseph Smith by the Angel Moroni. To play, mix up cards and lay them facedown on the floor or table. Divide children into two teams and have a teams take turns turning over two cards to make a match. Then read the match, telling what principle of the gospel was restored. The team with the most matches wins.

TO MAKE: Copy, color, and cut out the two sets of cards on cardstock and label that follow for each child. Enclose in a bag.

SCRIPTURE CHALLENGE: See p. 92, 94

THOUGHT TREAT (when appropriate): Gospel Granola. Give each child a granola bar and say, "Just as granola is made up of different ingredients like oats, sugar, nuts, and raisins that make it great, so is the gospel of Jesus Christ made up of several basic elements or ingredients to make it full and complete" (found on the match cards).

Lesson 4 — Prepare to Serve Jesus and Others

PREPARATION: Review Lesson 4 and enrichment activities 1-2 (p. 18) in Primary 5 D&C/Church History manual.

ACTIVITY: Prepare or Beware! Maze

Remind children that Jesus and others need their help. Ask them if they are ready to serve, and warn them to "Prepare or Beware! Don't get caught going in the wrong direction!" Work through maze to learn how to prepare.

TO MAKE: Copy, color, and cut out the maze that follows for each child.

SCRIPTURE CHALLENGE: See p. 92, 94

THOUGHT TREAT (when appropriate): Preparation Pickles. Give each child a pickle to eat and tell them, "Don't get yourself into a pickle . . . Be prepared." Explain that getting yourself into a pickle is getting into a bad situation. Jesus and Heavenly Father want us to be prepared by living the commandments.

Faith in Jesus Christ	Repentance	Baptism by Immersion
Gift of the Holy Ghost	Book of Mormon	Living Prophets
Priesthood Authority	Continuous Revelation	Temple Ordinances

| Lesson 5 | Heavenly Father Will Help Me as I Obey |

PREPARATION: Review Lesson 5 and enrichment activity 3 (p. 24) in the Primary 5 D&C/Church History manual.

ACTIVITY:
Message Dangler

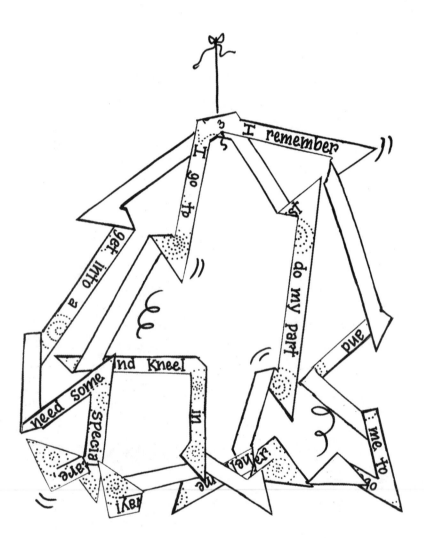

Children can dangle (hang) this message in their room to remind them that as they obey Heavenly Father's commandments, they can ask Him for help. He loves them and will help them find their way back to their heavenly home. To read message, start in the center with #1, then read 2, 3, and 4.

TO MAKE: Copy, color, and cut out the visual that follows for each child on cardstock paper, cutting only on heavy cutting lines. Bend corners (as shown above). Pierce a hole in the top (center) with a pencil. Tie a knot in a 12" string and thread through. You can add glitter to decorate.

SCRIPTURE CHALLENGE:
See p. 92, 95

THOUGHT TREAT (when appropriate): Endure-to-the-End Licorice. Children can eat a string of licorice rope and talk about enduring to the end (D&C 14:7).

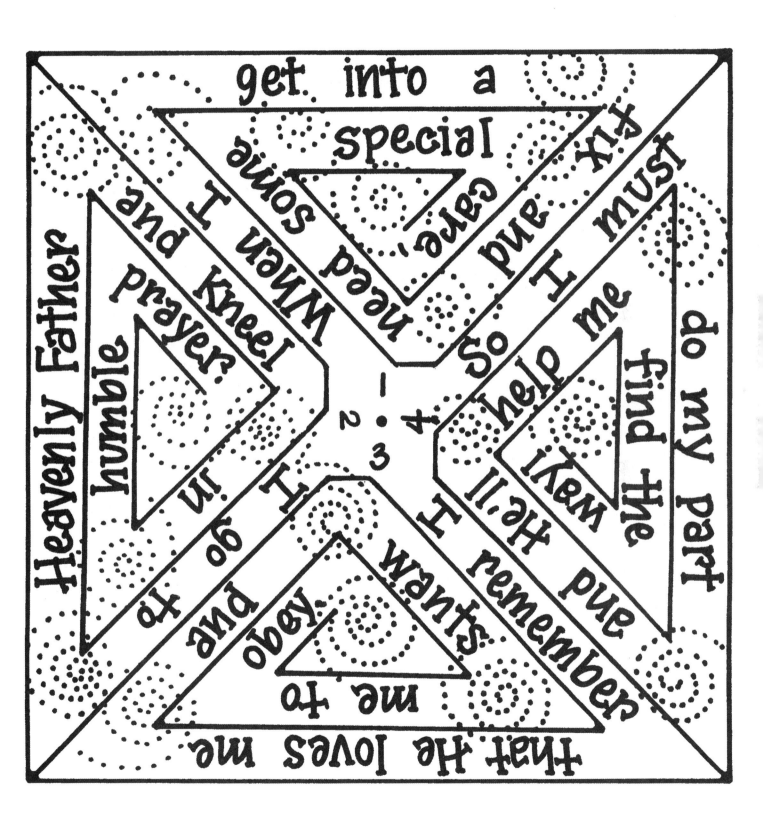

Lesson 6 — # Seeking Guidance Through Prayer

PREPARATION: Review Lesson 6 and enrichment activity 1 (p. 28) in the Primary 5 D&C/Church History manual.

ACTIVITY: Prayer Crossword Puzzle

Complete this prayer crossword puzzle with children to show them that answers to prayers come in many ways. Answer Key: Across: 5—Heavenly Father, 7—ask, 8—morning, 9—listen, 10—thank, 15—still small voice, 17—help. Down: 1—Holy Ghost, 2—prayer, 3—Jesus Christ, 4—yes, 6—guidance, 11—knees, 12—night, 13—blessings, 14—no, 18—peace.

TO MAKE: Copy, color, and cut out the puzzle that follows for each child on cardstock paper.

SCRIPTURE CHALLENGE: See p. 92, 95
THOUGHT TREAT (when appropriate): Prayer Popcorn. As children munch on popcorn, have them tell something they might ask Heavenly Father for or thank Him for. Tell children that just as heat warms kernels of corn before they pop, prayer warms our heart so messages from the Holy Ghost can "pop" into our mind.

Lesson 7 — # The Holy Ghost Will Guide and Comfort Me

PREPARATION: Review Lesson 7 and enrichment activity 5 (p. 34) in the Primary 5 D&C/Church History manual.

ACTIVITY: Invite the Spirit Game

Learn about choices that invite the Holy Ghost and choices that turn the Spirit away. Remind children that as we pray, we can ask for the Spirit to guide us to make right choices.
To Play: Children take turns drawing a wordstrip and reading it aloud. Player makes a choice by saying, "Invites the Spirit," or "Turns the Spirit Away." If competing in teams, award a point for each correct choice. When time is up, the team with the most points wins.

TO MAKE: Copy, color, and cut out the visual that follows for each child and place in a bag.

SCRIPTURE CHALLENGE: See p. 92, 96
THOUGHT TREAT (when appropriate): Smile-Frown Cookie. Frost a smile on top and a frown on bottom of cookie. Tell children, "When our choices invite the Spirit, we turn our frown upside down."

Puzzled about Prayer?

ACROSS

5. a parent (2 words)
7. request
8. early day
9. to hear
10. show gratitude
15. speaks to heart and mind (3 words)
17. aid

DOWN

1. spirit friend
2. kneeling activity
3. elder brother
4. affirmative
6. direction
11. prayer bones
12. days companion
13. count them
14. negative
16. the last word
18. war's opposite

Fold

Fold

give your dad a hug	pray with real intent
hurt someone just because they hurt you	be forgiving
feel happy when others are sad	take something without asking
volunteer and help an older person	thank your teacher for the lesson
be reverent in church	pay tithing on all money earned
take a toy away from your brother	take something without paying for it
help a brother or sister	wash dishes without being asked
tell someone he's dumb	tease your younger sister
frighten someone	tell a lie
miss family home evening	have family prayer
set the table for dinner	take out the garbage
skip doing homework	talk bad about a teacher
sass your mother	forgive someone
frown all day	go to bed on time and get up on time
go to bed after your bedtime	try to keep the Sabbath holy
read family events in your journal	help with family home evening
tell a friend you'll call but don't	don't obey all the commandments
spend your tithing money	be kind to animals
trust in others rather than Jesus	don't listen
don't help others when needed	spend time reading scriptures
care for others more than yourself	complain about doing your chores
take more food than you can eat	marry in the temple
serve a mission	see someone steal but don't tell anyone
tell a dirty joke	borrow a pen without returning it
talk during the sacrament	help a friend in need
ask a friend to come to church	make your brother's bed
ask your mother if you can help	cheer up the sad
go home "sick" when you really feel good	go somewhere without permission

Lesson 8   Being Worthy of Priesthood Blessings

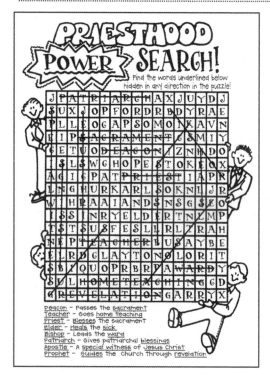

PREPARATION: Review Lesson 8 and enrichment activity 4 and 5 (p. 40) in the Primary 5 D&C/Church History manual.

ACTIVITY:
Priesthood Power Word Search

Search for words describing duties and various offices in the Aaronic and Melchizedek Priesthood. Cross through the words as you find them in any direction.

TO MAKE: Copy, color, and cut out the word search that follows for each child on cardstock paper.

SCRIPTURE CHALLENGE: See p. 92, 96

THOUGHT TREAT (when appropriate): Priesthood Pretzels. Give each child eight pretzels as you talk about the eight priesthood offices and duties found on the crossword puzzle.

Lesson 9   Testimony of Truth & The Book of Mormon

PREPARATION: Review Lesson 9 and testimony (p. 46) in the Primary 5 D&C/Church History manual.

ACTIVITY: Slide-show/Doorknob Hanger

Children place this bear around their bedroom doorknob to remind them of ways to be a witness of the Book of Mormon and its teachings. They can learn how to bear their testimony of the gospel of Christ.

TO MAKE: Copy, color, and cut out the visuals that follow for each child on cardstock paper. Boys glue bow tie on bear, and girls glue bow on head. Glue part A and B together where shown. Cut a slit in the top and bottom of square on bear's tummy. Slide doorknob hanger (slide-show wordstrips) down into bear to pull up and down. Fold bottom flap of wordstrip to prevent slipping.

SCRIPTURE CHALLENGE: See p. 92, 97

THOUGHT TREAT (when appropriate): Testimony-Bear Treats. Make bears out of traditional Rice Krispies, bread, or use cinnamon bear candies. Invite children to bear their testimony in class and then eat the bear treat.

PRIESTHOOD POWER SEARCH!

Find the words underlined below hidden in any direction in the puzzle!

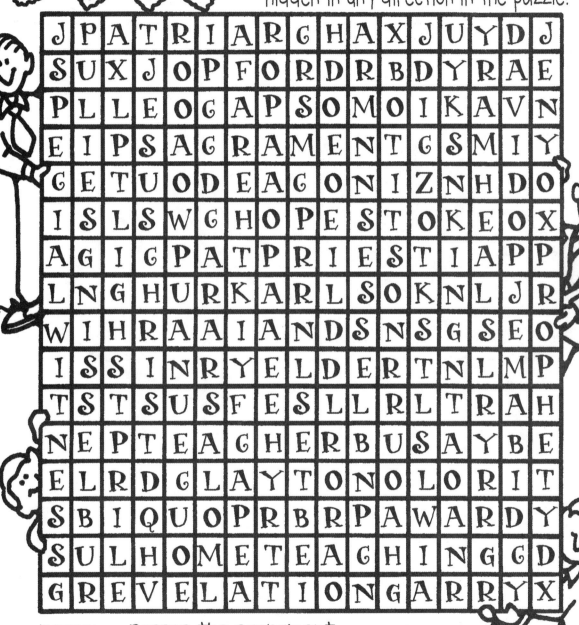

```
J P A T R I A R C H A X J U Y D J
S U X J O P F O R D R B D Y R A E
P L L E O C A P S O M O I K A V N
E I P S A C R A M E N T C S M I Y
C E T U O D E A C O N I Z N H D O
I S L S W C H O P E S T O K E O X
A G I C P A T P R I E S T I A P P
L N G H U R K A R L S O K N L J R
W I H R A A I A N D S N S G S E O
I S S I N R Y E L D E R T N L M P
T S T S U S F E S L L R L T R A H
N E P T E A C H E R B U S A Y B E
E L R D C L A Y T O N O L O R I T
S B I Q U O P R B R P A W A R D Y
S U L H O M E T E A C H I N G C D
G R E V E L A T I O N G A R R Y X
```

Deacon – Passes the <u>sacrament</u>
<u>Teacher</u> – Goes <u>home teaching</u>
<u>Priest</u> – <u>Blesses</u> the sacrament
<u>Elder</u> – <u>Heals</u> the <u>sick</u>
<u>Bishop</u> – Leads the <u>ward</u>
<u>Patriarch</u> – Gives patriarchal blessings
<u>Apostle</u> – A <u>special witness</u> of <u>Jesus Christ</u>
<u>Prophet</u> – <u>Guides</u> the Church through <u>revelation</u>

*Bow can be a bowtie for the boys and a hair bow for the girls.

I will "bear" my testimony of truth.

Glue to Part A

Joseph Smith translated the Book of Mormon through God's power.

The true priesthood was restored.

We have a living prophet today.

Jesus Christ lives and loves me.

The Holy Ghost speaks truth to my heart.

Fold Back

The Book of Mormon is true.

Joseph Smith is God's chosen prophet.

| Lesson 10 | Grateful for the Book of Mormon |

PREPARATION: Review Lesson 10 and preparation 3 and attention activity (p. 47) in the Primary 5 D&C/Church History manual.

ACTIVITY:
Typesetting Poster

1. Remind children that the Book of Mormon was first published by setting the metal type by hand. It was a lot of work, but it was worth the effort to make the Book of Mormon available to people everywhere.

2. Let children set type by placing the letters to read: "THE BOOK OF MORMON: ANOTHER TESTAMENT OF JESUS CHRIST" in the spaces provided on the poster. To typeset poster, have children cut out letters needed to "set the type," place spaces where necessary, then color the poster.

TO MAKE: Copy, color, and cut out the visuals that follow for each child.

SCRIPTURE CHALLENGE: See p. 92, 97

THOUGHT TREAT (when appropriate): Typesetter Pancakes. Ahead of time, shape and cook pancakes in letter shapes that start with something you might read in the Book of Mormon, e.g., "M" for Moroni, "T" tree of life. The batter could be colored to represent a person (pink), place (blue), thing (yellow). Children must find what they are eating in the book and read about it.

3 Nephi 11:10

"Behold, I am Jesus Christ, whom the prophets testified shall come into the world."

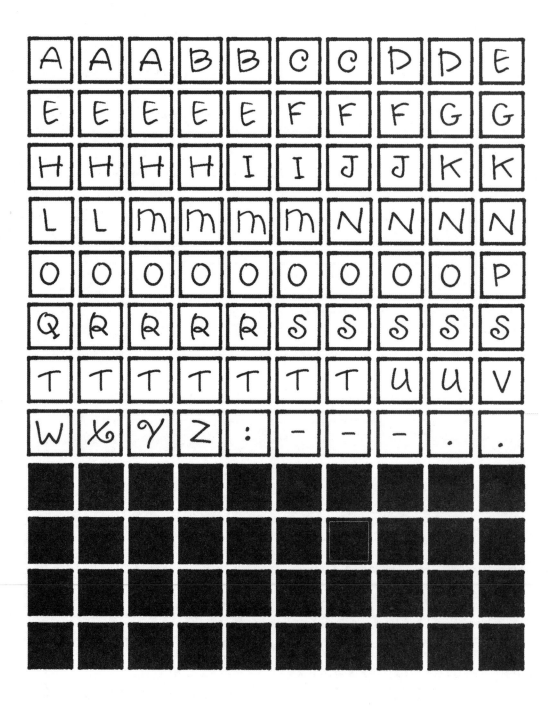

Lesson 11   True Church Was Restored to the Earth

PREPARATION: Review Lesson 11 and enrichment activities 3, 5, and 6 (p. 54-55) in the Primary 5 D&C/Church History manual.

ACTIVITY:
Then-and-Now Match Game

This match game helps children compare the gospel of Jesus Christ <u>then</u> (when Jesus came to earth), and <u>now</u> (when Joseph Smith restored the gospel in these latter days). Read the scriptures below and show Then and Now cards to learn about then and now.

To Play Game: Mix up cards, and lay face down on the floor or table. Divide children into two teams. Children take turns turning two cards over for all to see, saying "then" and/or "now" as they read: Baptism by Immersion ("then"/"now"), the Last Supper ("then"), Sacrament ("now"), etc. When a match is made, children collect the matching cards.
The team with the most matches wins.

TO MAKE: Copy, color, and cut out cards on cardstock that follow for each child.

SCRIPTURE CHALLENGE: See p. 92, 98

THOUGHT TREAT (when appropriate): Sweets. Give children candy, and tell them that the gospel is really sweet.

Then—Sermon on the Mount—Matthew 5:6 (Christ begins His ministry)
Now—First Vision—D&C 115:4, D&C 21:1, 3-4 (Christ restores His church to the earth)

Then—Jesus was baptized—Matthew 3:13, 16
Now—We are baptized—D&C 20:72-74

Then—Jesus ordained Apostles—Ephesians 2:19-20 (so Apostles could administer the priesthood),
Now—Melchizedek Priesthood restored—D&C 21:1 (so priesthood power can again

be on the earth) D&C 27:12 (128:20)
Then—Sacrament: Jesus blesses—Luke 22:19-20
Now—Sacrament: Members partake—D&C 20:75

Then—Jesus Christ is head of the Church—Amos 3:7
Now—Jesus Christ is head of the Church—D&C 21:5

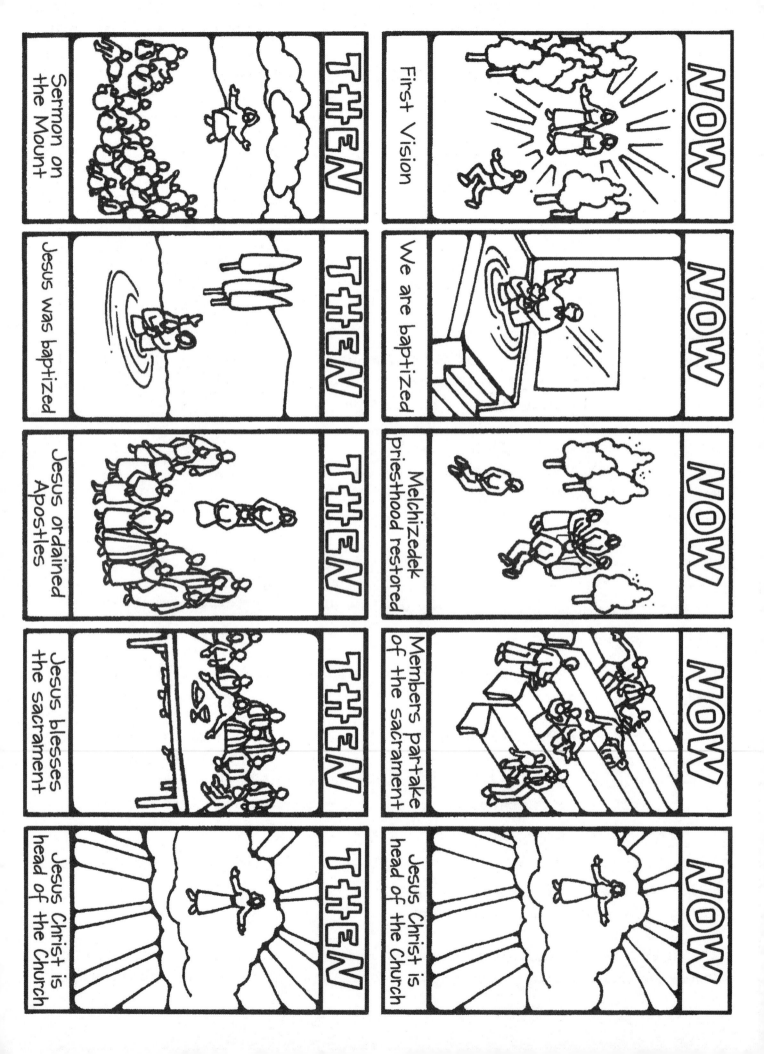

Lesson 12   # Grateful to Be Baptized

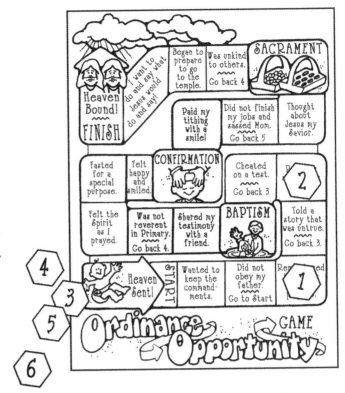

PREPARATION: Review Lesson 12 and attention activity (p. 57) and enrichment activity 2 (p. 61) in the Primary 5 D&C/Church History manual.

ACTIVITY:

Ordinance Opportunity Game

Help children learn about the ordinances that will help us return to our heavenly home and live with Heavenly Father again someday. By making right choices in our journey through life we can return.

● The ordinance of BAPTISM allows us to become a member of Jesus Christ's Church.

● The ordinances of CONFIRMATION allows us to receive the gift of the Holy Ghost to guide us.

● If we keep the commandments we can be worthy of the SACRAMENT ordinance that promises that the Spirit will continue to guide us.

● As we continue to keep the commandments, we can prepare to partake of TEMPLE ordinances, endowments, and sealings so we can be with our families forever. Then, after we finish our life here on earth, we can be part of Heavenly Father's kingdom.

To Play Game:

Place "MOVE" blocks (indicating number of spaces to move) in a bowl or hat. Divide class into two teams, using the #1 and #2 markers, or have more children play (up to 12 players can play using the #1-12 markers.)

Have children find their way back to their heavenly home by moving forward on the game board, trying to land on the right choices instead of the wrong. From a bowl or hat, take turns drawing a "MOVE" block, then moving the spaces designated from the START position. If they land on a wrong choice, they move back instead of forward on the next turn. The first person or team to reach heaven wins!

TO MAKE: Copy, color, and cut out the game and markers that follow for each child.

SCRIPTURE CHALLENGE: See p. 92, 98

THOUGHT TREAT (when appropriate): Ordinance Oatmeal Cookies. Place three raisins or chocolate chips on top of oatmeal cookies. Talk about the three ordinances in the game.

SACRAMENT

Heaven Bound! ~ FINISH

I want to do and say what Jesus would do and say!

Began to prepare to go to the temple.

Was unkind to others. ~ Go back 4

Paid my tithing with a smile!

Did not finish my jobs and sassed Mom. ~ Go back 5

Thought about Jesus my Savior.

Fasted for a special purpose.

Felt happy and smiled.

CONFIRMATION

Cheated on a test. ~ Go back 3

Read my scriptures daily.

Felt the Spirit as I prayed.

Was not reverent in Primary. ~ Go back 4.

Shared my testimony with a friend.

BAPTISM

Told a story that was untrue. ~ Go back 3.

Heaven Sent! START

Wanted to keep the commandments.

Did not obey my father. ~ Go to Start

Remembered to say my morning prayers.

Ordinance Opportunity GAME

1	2	3	4	5	6
7	8	9	10	11	12

Move 1	Move 2	Move 3	Move 4
Move 1	Move 2	Move 3	Move 4
Move 1	Move 2	Move 3	Move 4
Move 1	Move 2	Move 3	Move 4
Move 1	Move 2	Move 3	Move 4
Move 1	Move 2	Move 3	Move 4
Move 1	Move 2	Move 3	Move 4
Move 1	Move 2	Move 3	Move 4
Move 1	Move 2	Move 3	Move 4

| Lesson 13 | Sharing the Gospel of Jesus Christ |

PREPARATION: Review Lesson 13 enrichment activities 5 (p. 69) in the Primary 5 D&C/Church History manual.

ACTIVITY:
Bendable Missionary Dolls

These dolls will remind children of the qualities they can develop to be a successful missionary: knowledge, diligence, virtue, brotherly kindness, temperance, charity, faith, patience, godliness, and humility.

TO MAKE: Copy, color, and cut out a girl or boy doll for each child on cardstock paper. Glue or tape pipe cleaners or wire on the inside of doll parts to connect parts. Then fold front over pipe cleaner or wire and glue parts in place. Bend so missionary will sit on scriptures to remind children to read them!

SCRIPTURE CHALLENGE: See p. 92, 99
THOUGHT TREAT (when appropriate): Gingerbread Missionary.

| Lesson 14 | Sacred Hymns Bring Blessings |

PREPARATION: Review Lesson 14 and enrichment activities 1 and 5 (p. 73-74) in the Primary 5 D&C/Church History manual.

ACTIVITY: "Note"able Hymns Secret Code Message

Using the code breaker, have children find the hidden messages that tell us the kinds of blessings we receive from singing hymns. Answers: Strengthen our faith, teach us the gospel, help us want to repent, help us choose the right, make us feel happy, and help to give us good thoughts.

TO MAKE: Copy, color, and cut out the visual that follows for each child on cardstock paper.

SCRIPTURE CHALLENGE: See p. 92, 99
THOUGHT TREAT (when appropriate): Note Cookies. Frost a music note on each cookie.

notable HYMNS

Using the code below, find out what kinds of blessings we receive from singing hymns!

A C D E F G H I K L M N O P R S T U V W Y

Lesson 15   The Prophet Speaks and I Listen

PREPARATION: Review Lesson 15 and discussion and application question 4 (p. 78) in the Primary 5 D&C/Church History manual.

ACTIVITY: Revelation Routes

On the poster have children draw an arrow from each person to the people he or she receives revelation for. For example, the prophet receives revelation for the whole Church, so draw a line from the prophet to everyone except Heavenly Father and Jesus Christ.

TO MAKE: Copy, color, and cut out the visual that follows for each child.

SCRIPTURE CHALLENGE: See p. 92, 100

THOUGHT TREAT (when appropriate): Revelation Pretzels. Purchase or make large straight or twisted pretzel shapes. As children eat straight pretzels, remind them that the prophet reveals to us ways we can follow the straight and narrow path back to heaven. As children eat the twisted pretzels, remind them that without the prophet to guide us, we might get off the straight and narrow path and become lost. Say, "Let's listen to the prophet's voice to stay on the path, gain eternal life, and live with Heavenly Father again."

Lesson 16   Love and Unity Help Others

PREPARATION: Review Lesson 16 and attention activity (p. 80), discussion and application question 7 (p. 83—D&C 38:27), and enrichment activity 1 (p. 83) in the Primary 5 D&C/Church History manual.

ACTIVITY: Woven-Heart Message

This woven heart will help children think of ways they can inspire love and unity at church and at home.

TO MAKE: Copy, color, and cut out the visual that follows for each child on cardstock paper. Cut out heart halves and cut along thin lines to weave halves together. Weave and glue ends so heart will not separate. As children weave, have them think of ways they can inspire love and unity.

SCRIPTURE CHALLENGE: See p. 92, 100

THOUGHT TREAT (when appropriate): Heart-Shaped Candy or Cookies.

Me!

Heavenly Father & Jesus Christ

Bishop

Primary Teacher

Mother & Father

Prophet

The Ward

Brother & Sister

Revelation Routes!

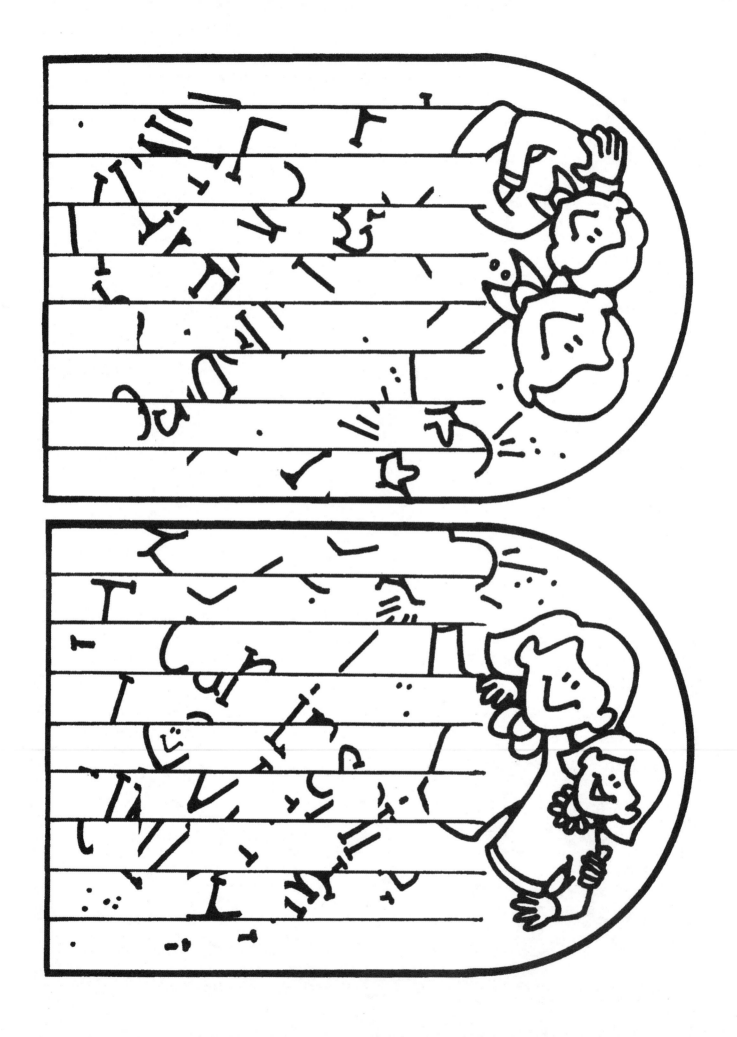

| Lesson 17 | Supporting Church Leaders |

PREPARATION: Review Lesson 17 and enrichment activity 2 in the Primary 5 D&C/Church History manual.

ACTIVITY: Bishop Bingo

Play Bishop Bingo to help children learn the various things a bishop or his counselors might do to guide us. To Play: (1) Give each child a different card if playing with eight children. If more than eight children play, let them know that another child may have a card that matches the one they have. (2) Give each child 10 or more markers (candy, beans, etc.). (3) Children can take turns drawing clues from a hat or box and calling the bingo square. (4) When a player's bingo card picture matches the clue, the player can cover the square with a marker. (5) Play until winner has a row of five marked squares (left, right, or diagonal) and announces "Bishop Bingo!"

TO MAKE: Copy, color, and cut out the cards and clues that follow, having one card per child. Place clues (below) in a hat or box to draw from.

SCRIPTURE CHALLENGE: See p. 92, 101

THOUGHT TREAT (when appropriate): Sweet Blessings Cookie. Give children a sugar cookie and talk about the sweet blessings the bishop brings to your ward or branch family. Also say, "The sweet taste of this cookie makes us feel happy. The sweet testimony that the bishop and his counselors share gives us a happy, peaceful feeling."

Wants you to choose the right	Conducts temple interview	Supervises leaders
Receives revelation	Has a testimony	Prays for the ward
Conducts interview for baptism	Can be a friend	Fasts for the ward
Shakes your hand	Gives a member a calling	Gives a blessing
Helps members repent	Visits the sick	Can help with problems
Can be a good example	Conducts meetings	Counsels a member
Greets with a smile	Accepts your tithing	Loves the ward
Helps a needy family	Visits a ward member	Teaches the gospel

BISHOP BINGO

Supervises leaders	Prays for the ward	Has a testimony	Conducts temple interview	Wants you to choose the right (CTR)
Loves the ward	Greets with a smile	Receives revelation	Helps a needy family	Can be a good example
Fasts for the ward	Gives a blessing	**FREE!**	Helps members repent	Shakes your hand
Can help with problems	Gives a member a calling	Conducts interview for baptism	Teaches the gospel	Accepts your tithing
Visits the sick	Counsels a member	Conducts meetings	Can be a friend	Visits a ward member

Card 1

BISHOP BINGO

Receives revelation	Supervises leaders	Visits a ward member	Gives a blessing	Fasts for the ward
Greets with a smile	Wants you to choose the right (CTR)	Prays for the ward	Conducts temple interview	Loves the ward
Conducts interview for baptism	**FREE!**	Accepts your tithing	Can help with problems	Helps a needy family
Shakes your hand	Can be a good example	Counsels a member	Has a testimony	Conducts meetings
Visits the sick	Gives a member a calling	Helps members repent	Can be a friend	Teaches the gospel

Card 2

BISHOP BINGO

Card 3

Accepts your tithing	Visits a ward member	Conducts meetings	Can be a friend	Conducts temple interview
Supervises leaders	Prays for the ward	Visits the sick	Has a testimony	Gives a member a calling
Gives a blessing	Can be a good example	FREE!	Shakes your hand	Greets with a smile
Teaches the gospel	Wants you to choose the right (CTR)	Helps members repent	Conducts interview for baptism	Receives revelation
Fasts for the ward	Loves the ward	Helps a needy family	Counsels a member	Can help with problems

BISHOP BINGO

Card 4

Has a testimony	Can be a friend	Wants you to choose the right (CTR)	Can be a good example	Greets with a smile
Visits the sick	Accepts your tithing	Helps members repent	Conducts interview for baptism	Receives revelation
Conducts temple interview	Conducts meetings	FREE!	Can help with problems	Loves the ward
Prays for the ward	Gives a member a calling	Shakes your hand	Counsels a member	Gives a blessing
Visits a ward member	Supervises leaders	Fasts for the ward	Helps a needy family	Teaches the gospel

BISHOP BINGO

Card 5

Loves the ward	Greets with a smile	Helps members repent	Conducts interview for baptism	Receives revelation
Teaches the gospel	Can be a good example	Shakes your hand	Can be a friend	Helps a needy family
Supervises leaders	Can help with problems	FREE!	Gives a member a calling	Wants you to choose the right (CTR)
Gives a blessing	Prays for the ward	Visits the sick	Has a testimony	Conducts temple interview
Fasts for the ward	Counsels a member	Visits a ward member	Conducts meetings	Accepts your tithing

BISHOP BINGO

Card 6

Shakes your hand	Wants you to choose the right (CTR)	Can be a good example	Gives a blessing	Helps members repent
Can be a friend	Receives revelation	Greets with a smile	Conducts interview for baptism	Teaches the gospel
Has a testimony	Helps a needy family	FREE!	Accepts your tithing	Loves the ward
Gives a member a calling	Conducts temple interview	Fasts for the ward	Conducts meetings	Can help with problems
Visits the sick	Prays for the ward	Visits a ward member	Supervises leaders	Counsels a member

BISHOP BINGO

Card 7

Teaches the gospel	Loves the ward	Conducts interview for baptism	Supervises leaders	Helps members repent
Fasts for the ward	Helps a needy family	Greets with a smile	Wants you to choose the right (CTR)	Shakes your hand
Gives a member a calling	Receives revelation	FREE!	Has a testimony	Can be a good example
Can help with problems	Conducts temple interview	Prays for the ward	Visits the sick	Conducts meetings
Gives a blessing	Counsels a member	Can be a friend	Visits a ward member	Accepts your tithing

BISHOP BINGO

Card 8

Conducts interview for baptism	Helps members repent	Shakes your hand	Counsels a member	Receives revelation
Can be a good example	Supervises leaders	Wants you to choose the right (CTR)	Helps a needy family	Loves the ward
Greets with a smile	Can be a friend	FREE!	Has a testimony	Gives a blessing
Accepts your tithing	Gives a member a calling	Visits the sick	Conducts temple interview	Teaches the gospel
Conducts meetings	Visits a ward member	Fasts for the ward	Can help with problems	Prays for the ward

| Lesson 18 | Building Up the Kingdom of God |

PREPARATION: Review Lesson 18 and enrichment activity 1 (p. 94) in the Primary 5 D&C/Church History manual.

ACTIVITY:
Law of Consecration Checkbook

This checkbook helps children learn about the law of consecration, to give of their time, talents, and means to build up the kingdom of God on the earth. Children can fill in date and name of the person they are giving the checkbook to, e.g., Mom or Dad. On the "For" line they write what service they did (giving of their time, talents, or means). They can report past experiences.

LAW OF CONSECRATION AREAS:

- Time: Visit the lonely, cheer someone who is sad, read to a brother or sister, sweep the floor, play with the baby, listen to someone, or babysit so parents can attend the temple.
- Talents: Play the piano, paint a picture, help Mother lift or move heavy things, help make a quilt for someone in need, or sing baby sister to sleep.
- Means: Giving of tithing, fast offering, missionary fund, or food and clothing to needy.

TO MAKE: Copy, color, and cut out the visuals that follow for each child on cardstock paper. Staple checkbook with Consecration Checkbook as the cover.

SCRIPTURE CHALLENGE: See p. 92, 101

THOUGHT TREAT (when appropriate): Double-Share Treats. Share a treat with the children and provide enough for each child to share with someone in need.

| Lesson 19 | Recognizing True Gifts of the Spirit |

PREPARATION: Review Lesson 19 and enrichment activity 1 (p. 101) in the Primary 5 D&C/Church History manual.

ACTIVITY: Gifts Match Game

Have children draw a line from the scripture to the gift (of the Spirit) found in the scripture. Talk about the gifts and why it is important to recognize and seek true gifts.

TO MAKE: Copy, color, and cut out the visual that follows for each child.

SCRIPTURE CHALLENGE: See p. 92, 102

THOUGHT TREAT (when appropriate): Gift Gumdrops. Children can name the six gifts before eating six gumdrops.

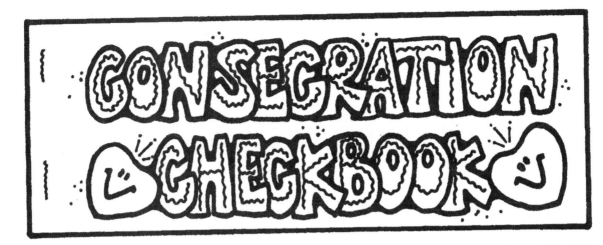

CONSECRATION CHECKBOOK

TIME

Date: _____

To: _____

For: _____

Sign: _____

TALENT

Date: _____

To: _____

For: _____

Sign: _____

MEANS

Date: _____

To: _____

For: _____

Sign: _____

Gifts of the Spirit

Fill in the blank and match the gift with the correct reference.

D&C 46:22

D&C 46:24-25

D&C 46: 17-18

D&C 46:14

D&C 46:19-20

D&C 46:13

° Gifts of w_____ and k_____.

° Gift to _____ the testimony of others.

° Gifts of faith to ____ and be _____.

° Gift of p_____.

° Gift to ____ that Jesus is the _____.

° Gift to s____ and understand languages.

Lesson 20	Love to Study the Scriptures

PREPARATION: Review Lesson 20 and enrichment activity 5 (p. 108) in the Primary 5 D&C/Church History manual.

ACTIVITY:
Scattered Scriptures Mix-n-Match

Increase a child's love for the scriptures by mixing and matching these scriptures. But watch out! These dual-match cards may fool you (e.g., the "if ye love me" card could also match with the "bring to pass the immortality and eternal life of man" card, but it doesn't. It matches with the "keep my commandments" card).

To Match Cards: Mix up cards in two separate piles facedown on the table or floor as follows. Card Pile 1: Place cards with capitol letters on left. Card Pile 2: Place other cards on the right. Take turns picking up two cards (one from each pile) to make a scripture match. Read matched cards aloud.

TO MAKE: Copy, color, and cut out the visuals that follow for each child.

SCRIPTURE CHALLENGE: See p. 92, 102

THOUGHT TREAT (when appropriate): Standard Works Bite-size Cookies. Stack four graham crackers or wafer-type cookies on top of each other with frosting (for display only). The four cookies represent the four standard works. Tell children that eating the stack all at once would be hard, but bit by bit it would be easy, just like reading the scriptures. Give children one cookie with frosting.

Lesson 21	Forgiving Others and Finding Peace

PREPARATION: Review Lesson 21 and home reading (p. 114) in the Primary 5 D&C/Church History manual.

ACTIVITY: Bite-size Memorize

Memorize scripture and talk about how we forgive.
TO MAKE: Copy, color, and cut out visual for each child.

SCRIPTURE CHALLENGE: See p. 92, 103
THOUGHT TREAT (when appropriate): Disappearing Candy. Give children a soft buttermint or piece of candy that melts quickly. Talk about how feelings melt quickly when we forgive.

For behold, I, God, have suffered these things for all,...

...that they might not suffer if they would repent.

D&C 19:16

Wherefore, be of good cheer, and do not fear,...

...for I the Lord am with you, and will stand by you.

D&C 68:6

Be patient in afflictions for thou shalt have many; but endure them,...

...for, lo, I am with thee, even unto the end of thy days.

D&C 24:8

I ,the Lord, am bound when ye do what I say;...

...but when ye do not what I say, ye have no promise.

D&C 82:10

Wherefore, be not weary in well-doing, for ye are laying the foundation of a great work.

And out of small things proceedeth that which is great.

D&C 64:33

Therefore, care not for the body, neither the life of the body...

...but care for the soul, and for the life of the soul.

D&C 101:37

He that findeth his life shall lose it...

...and he that loseth his life for my sake shall find it.

Matt. 10:39

Choose you this day whom ye will serve...

...but as for me and my house, we will serve the Lord.

Joshua 24:15

For if ye forgive men their trespasses...

...your heavenly Father will also forgive you.

Matt. 6:14

If ye love me,...

...keep my commandments.

John 14:15

Lay not up for yourselves treasures upon earth,...

...But lay up for yourselves treasures in heaven.

Matt. 6:19-20

This is my work and my glory — ...

...to bring to pass the immortality and eternal life of man.

Moses 1:39

Faith is not to have a perfect knowledge of things;...

...therefore if ye have faith ye hope for things which are not seen, which are true.

Alma 32:21

Adam fell that men might be;...

...and men are, that they might have joy.

2 Nephi 2:25

Verily, verily, I say unto you, ye must watch and pray always;...

...lest ye be tempted by the devil, and ye be led away captive by him.

3 Nephi 18:15

For behold, this life is the time for men to prepare to meet God;...

...yea, behold the day of this life is the day for men to perform their labors.

Alma 34:32

And it came to pass that there was no contention in the land;...

...because of the love of God which did dwell in the hearts of the people.

4 Nephi 1:15

But charity is the pure love of Christ, and it endureth forever;...

...and whoso is found possessed of it at the last day, it shall be well with him.

Moroni 7:47

Bite-size Memorize

I, the Lord, 4-give whom I 4-give, but of you it is re---d 2 4-give all.

D&C 64:10

Prophets Giving Revelations

PREPARATION: Review Lesson 22 and enrichment activity 1 (p. 118) in the Primary 5 D&C/Church History manual.

ACTIVITY:
Standard-Works Thinkathon Game

Help children learn the purpose of the standard works: Bible, Book of Mormon, Doctrine and Covenants, and Pearl of Great Price. The Standard-Works Thinkathon Game will help children become more familiar with the standard works, which contain the words of the prophets and testify of Jesus Christ and His gospel. Before playing, talk about the standard works, telling children that the prophets of each time period told about their people, their faith, and their knowledge of Jesus Christ. Read and talk about each wordstrip, then have a quiz by playing the game.

TO MAKE: Copy, color, and cut out the visual and wordstrips that follow and game rules (below) for each child (copy block on cardstock paper). Fold box and glue tabs inside. Place wordstrips inside plastic bag with game rules.

SCRIPTURE CHALLENGE: See p. 92, 103

THOUGHT TREAT (when appropriate): Footstep Graham Crackers. Frost a footprint on top of a graham cracker. Tell children that if they read the scriptures they will learn how to follow in the footsteps of Jesus. Read 1 Nephi 3:7 and tell children that the Lord will prepare a way for us to obey the commandments and to follow in His steps, which will lead us on the straight and narrow path back to heaven.

. . . .

Standard Works Thinkathon Game Rules

1. Divide players into two teams and have one team member at a time represent each team. Teams take turns, one team member at a time answering the question.

2. Teams take turns drawing a question and handing it to leader to read.
3. Player has 10 seconds to answer by guessing Book of Mormon, Pearl of Great Price, Doctrine and Covenants, or Bible. If not answered, the question is given to the other team to guess.
4. Once a correct answer is given, the team can roll the box to determine if they receive a point or not. If they roll the book that matches their answer, they receive a point. For example, if the answer was BIBLE, they must roll a BIBLE to earn the point. If they roll BONUS, they receive 2 points. If they roll ROLL AGAIN, they get another chance to win a point. When time is up, or all scriptures are drawn, the team with the most points wins!

. . . .

Which book tells us about the prophecies of Jesus Christ? **BIBLE** and **BOOK OF MORMON**	Which book contains the sacrament prayers? **DOCTRINE AND COVENANTS** and **BOOK OF MORMON**
Which book tells about the Savior's life and teachings when He was on the earth? **BIBLE**	Which book tells of the restoration of the Aaronic priesthood by John the Baptist? **DOCTRINE AND COVENANTS**
Which book is another testament of Jesus Christ? **BOOK OF MORMON**	Which book tells of qualities of a missionary? **DOCTRINE AND COVENANTS**
Which book tells about the Savior's dealings with the people on the American continent? **BOOK OF MORMON**	Which book tells of the prophet receiving revelation for the whole Church? **DOCTRINE AND COVENANTS**
Which book is a collection of revelations from Jesus Christ for the latter day, our times? **DOCTRINE AND COVENANTS**	Which book tells these stories: Shadrach, Meshach, and Abednego, Jonah and the whale, and David and Goliath? **BIBLE**
Which book gives us teachings and testimonies of Jesus Christ from ancient prophets as well as Joseph Smith's history and his testimony of Heavenly Father and Jesus Christ? **PEARL OF GREAT PRICE**	Which book contains translations from the ancient writings of Abraham? (These records were found in the catacombs of Egypt.) **PEARL OF GREAT PRICE**
Which book tells the most about the Lord and His people in the Holy Land, beginning with the earth's creation? **BIBLE**	Which book told the stories of Alma the Younger and Amulek, peace in America, and crossing the sea to the promised land? **BOOK OF MORMON**
Which book tells of Jesus Christ visiting the people of the American continent? **BOOK OF MORMON**	Which book tells of Enos, King Benjamin, Abinadi and King Noah, and Helaman and the 2,000 young men? **BOOK OF MORMON**
Which book tells the most about the birth of Jesus and His life on the earth? **BIBLE**	Which book tells of the three kingdoms of heaven? **DOCTRINE AND COVENANTS**
Which book has a record of Heavenly Father and Jesus Christ appearing to Joseph Smith in the Sacred Grove? **PEARL OF GREAT PRICE**	Which book contains Joseph Smith's translations of the book of Matthew (from the Bible)? **PEARL OF GREAT PRICE**
Which book tells how the Church should be established in the last days? **DOCTRINE AND COVENANTS**	Which book tells the stories of Adam and Eve, Noah and the ark, Joseph sold into Egypt, the ten commandments, and Queen Esther? **BIBLE**
Which book testifies of Jesus Christ visiting the people in Ancient America? **BOOK OF MORMON**	Which book contains the Book of Moses (parts of the Bible) translated by Joseph Smith? **PEARL OF GREAT PRICE**
Which book tells about the Word of Wisdom? **DOCTRINE AND COVENANTS**	Which book contains the Articles of Faith? **PEARL OF GREAT PRICE**

Lesson 23 Celestial Life with Heavenly Father & Jesus

PREPARATION: Review Lesson 23 and attention activity (p. 121–122) and suggested family sharing (p. 125) in the Primary 5 D&C/Church History manual.

ACTIVITY: Connected Kingdoms

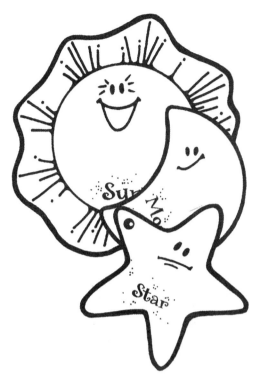

Help children choose to live again with Heavenly Father and Jesus Christ in the celestial kingdom by comparing the three possible places they could live after this earth life. Children can share this teaching tool with friends.

TO MAKE: Copy, color, and cut out the visuals that follow for each child on cardstock paper. Cut inside border lines on description and outside border lines on images so they will fit. Glue kingdom descriptions on back of the matching kingdom. Place a metal or button brad through holes to attach moon and stars to sun. To make button brad, sew two buttons together on opposite sides, threading thread through the same hole to attach kingdom pieces.

SCRIPTURE CHALLENGE: See p. 92, 104

THOUGHT TREAT (when appropriate): Celestial Soda. Provide a straw and pop-can (or cup) for each child. Reduce the celestial sun visual that follows 50% and copy the note below. Then mount sun on the straw by paper punching two holes in top and bottom to insert into straw. Glue note below on pop can (or cup). Read note as you sip the soda.

> *"As we sip this 'celestial soda,' let's imagine what it would be like to live with Heavenly Father and Jesus and our families forever. We are created in Heavenly Father's image and we can become like Him. Our goal is to get back to heaven to live in the celestial kingdom. So let's say each day, 'I AM HEAVEN-SENT AND HEAVEN-BOUND'"*

CELESTIAL KINGDOM
Glory compared to brightness of sun—highest kingdom
(D&C 76:91). People who have been baptized and confirmed
and keep the commandments will live here (D&C 76:50-52).
1. They will live with Heavenly Father and Jesus Christ
   forever (D&C 76:50-52).
2. They will become like Heavenly Father (D&C 76:58; 131:20).
3. They will live with their righteous family members*
   (D&C 131:2-4).
4. They will receive a fulness of joy (D&C 138:17). There are
   three heavens or degrees in the celestial kingdom
   (D&C 131:1). To live in the highest kingdom, one must
   make sacred covenants, promises, be married, and be
   sealed to our families for eternity (D&C 131:2-3).
   *The highest degree is the only place
   families can live together forever.

TELESTIAL KINGDOM
Glory compared to the brightness of a star—the lowest kingdom.
Those who did not accept the brightness of the gospel of Jesus
testimony of Jesus: liars, sorcerers, adulterers, whoremongers,
Thrust down to hell, redeemed of the Lord in the last
resurrection. The Holy Ghost and angels
will minister to these people. They
and Jesus but will know of Heavenly Father.
live with them or see them.
They won't be able to live with
their families. D&C 76:81;103

TERRESTIAL
KINGDOM
Glory compared to the brightness of
the moon—the middle kingdom (D&C 76:72-91).
These people are those who die without the law.
Jesus will visit the people here. They will know of
Heavenly Father but will never live with Him. They
do not receive a testimony of Jesus in the flesh, but
after death receive a testimony. Lived honorably, but
blinded by the craftiness of men, not valiant in the
testimony of Jesus. *These people won't be able to
live with their
families.

Lesson 24   Say "No" to Harmful & "Yes" to Healthful

PREPARATION: Review Lesson 24 and review enrichment activities 3 and 4 (p. 131) in the Primary 5 D&C/Church History manual.

ACTIVITY:
Word of Wisdom Voting Ballot

Have children read the statement and vote "yes" or "no" by checking the column next to the statement. This will help children make healthful decisions. They can look up the scriptures and fill in the blanks.

TO MAKE: Copy, color, and cut out the voting ballot that follows for each child.

SCRIPTURE CHALLENGE: See p. 92, 104

THOUGHT TREAT (when appropriate): Healthful Choice Food. Talk about the variety of foods we have to choose from that are healthful. Bless the food and thank Heavenly Father for the healthful choices we have and for the revelation of the Word of Wisdom given to us through the Prophet Joseph Smith.

Lesson 25   We Are Blessed When We Sacrifice

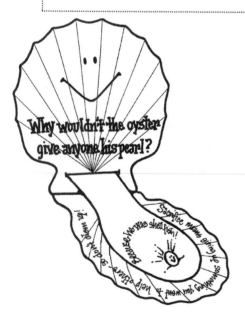

PREPARATION: Review Lesson 25 and enrichment activity 4 (p. 137) in the Primary 5 D&C/Church History manual.

ACTIVITY: Giving Oyster Mirror Motivator

Children can post this shell on their mirror to remind them not to be selfish, to sacrifice their time, talents, and means to build up the kingdom of God as the pioneers did. Review Lesson 18, activity 1, p. 94 in the manual.

TO MAKE: Copy, color, and cut out the visual that follows for each child. Crease shell lines to create a 3-D effect. Cut slits in A and B to attach oyster to shell. Glue oyster pieces together as indicated, except for tab B. Insert tabs where indicated and glue in place.

SCRIPTURE CHALLENGE: See p. 92, 105

THOUGHT TREAT (when appropriate): Sacrifice Soda-crackers. Tell children that it took time, talent, and means to make these crackers. Likewise, we can give of ourselves to help and serve others.

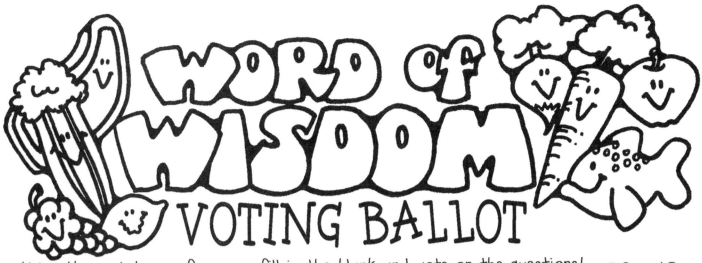

WORD of WISDOM VOTING BALLOT

Using the scripture references, fill in the blank and vote on the questions!

YES   NO

- Will I use the _____ of beasts and of _____ sparingly? (D&C 89:12)   ⬡ ⬡

- Will I use wholesome _____ God ordained for man? (D&C 89:10)   ⬡ ⬡

- Will I eat plenty of _____s and _____s? (D&C 89:16)   ⬡ ⬡

- Will I use hot _____? Are they good for my belly? (D&C 89:9)   ⬡ ⬡

- Will I eat _____ that is made both for ___ and _____ of the field? (D&C 89:14)   ⬡ ⬡

- Some may tempt me to take strong _____. What will I say? (D&C 89:7)   ⬡ ⬡

- The use of _____ is for sick cattle. Is it for the body? Will I use it? (D&C 89:8)   ⬡ ⬡

- Will I obey the Word of Wisdom and receive its promise? I'll receive _____ in the navel and _____ in the bones, I'll ___ and not be weary and _____ and not faint. (D&C 89:18-20)   ⬡ ⬡

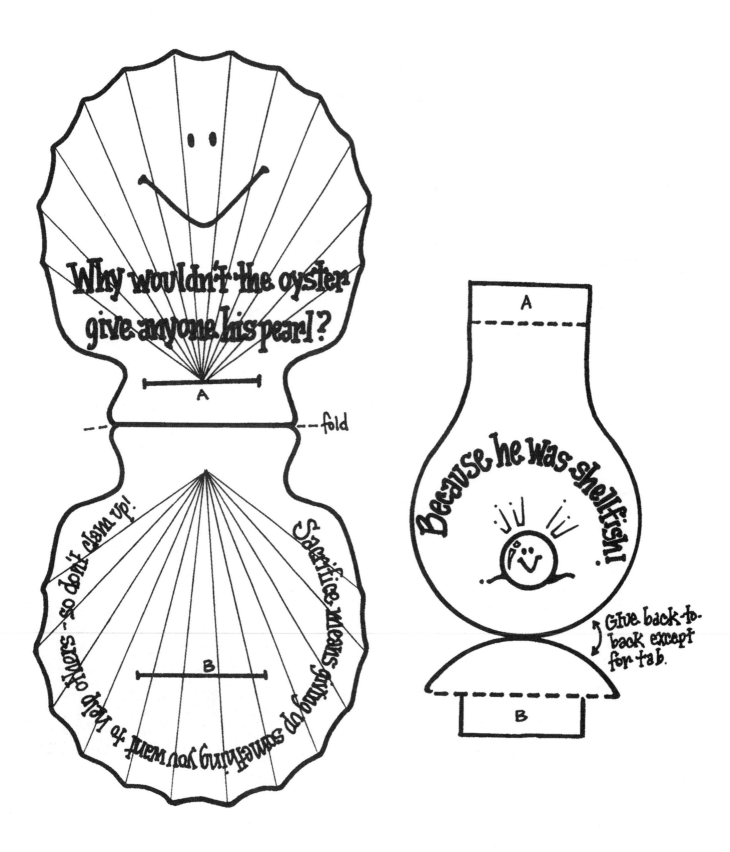

Lesson 26   Unlock the Powers of Heaven

PREPARATION: Review Lesson 26 and attention activity (page 139) and discussion and application questions (page 142) in the Primary 5 D&C/Church History manual.

ACTIVITY: Priesthood Keys Door Reminder

Remind children that Joseph Smith and Oliver Cowdery unlocked the powers of heaven when they received the priesthood keys from the prophets Moses and Elijah. These keys help us do missionary and temple work. Read the scriptures on each key to know who restored which priesthood key, Moses or Elijah.

TO MAKE: Copy, color, and cut out the visuals that follow for each child on cardstock paper. When cutting out, cut out Moses and Elijah figures and glue on the right key. Glue keys back-to-back. Punch a hole in keys and tie on a 12" string. Attach keys to your bedroom door to remind you of the priesthood keys that will unlock the powers of heaven.

SCRIPTURE CHALLENGE: See p. 92, 105

THOUGHT TREAT (when appropriate): Cloud 9 Pudding. Top pudding with whipped cream to remind children of that "Cloud 9" feeling that comes from heavenly priesthood blessings.

Lesson 27   We Are Blessed as We Obey

PREPARATION: Review Lesson 27 and enrichment activity 4 (page 152) in the Primary 5 D&C/Church History manual.

ACTIVITY: Blackout! Promise Puzzle

Challenge children to find a very special promise for keeping the commandments. Follow directions to find the message: "I the Lord . . . promise."

TO MAKE: Copy, color, and cut out the puzzle that follows for each child. Provide pencils.

SCRIPTURE CHALLENGE: See p. 92, 106

THOUGHT TREAT (when appropriate): Testimony Treats. Award children with one treat for every commandment they can list on board, and two for listing how they can obey this commandment.

BLACKOUT! PROMISE PUZZLE

Using the clues below, color in the square indicated using the coordinates A-J and 1-20. The squares left in order will spell out a scripture with a very special promise. After you have figured out a key word, use the Topical Guide to find the reference.

	1	2	3	4	5	6	7	8	9	10	11	12	13	14	15	16	17	18	19	20
A		I		T	H				E			L							O	
B	R		D		A	M	B			O	U		N							
C		D		D	W		H	E		N		Y							E	
D						O			W			H		A						
E	T			I		S	A				Y		B	U						
F	T		W			H	E			N		Y	E						D	
G	O		N		O			T			W	H		A	T					
H	I		S		A	Y	Y		E			H			A	V				
I	E			N					O				P		R					
J	O		M		I		S	E												

D&C 82 : 10

Blackout Clues: E12, G13, I5, H5, E4, I15, C17, B20, F17, G16, H13, I14, J16, E7, D11 E5, D6, I20, G1, D5, J20, A17, C4, D3, H15, G4, A16, E17, F3, D1, J3, D20, E2, I8, J13, H17, F19, D15, D19, B17, F13, H6, I7, J15, C11, C16, E14, G9, F5, F11, I16, C18, D14, B13, J11, A9, G8, D7, G3, H10, J1, I3, B3, A20, D13, F2, H16, E3, H2, J2, C19, G8, A4, G6, I18, E16, I4, D17, J6, F7, A14, E13, G20, J19, A1, C2, C1, J5, G12, G17, A2, I1, I10, J17, A10, B1, H12, A13, B5, D8, J8, I9, A7, J18, A5, B6, D9, E8, H3, E11, A18, C7, B8, C5, A11, G10, B14, B12, D4, F6, F10, I11, J9, B10, E20, B19, C14, I12, F18, H19, F14, C13

D&C 110:13-16 Restored the keys of the sealing power so families can be together forever!

MOSES

ELIJAH

D&C 110:11 Restored the keys of the gathering of Israel so missionaries can bring people into the church!

BLACKOUT! PROMISE PUZZLE

Using the clues below, color in the square indicated using the coordinates A–J and 1–20. The squares left in order will spell out a scripture with a very special promise. After you have figured out a key word, use the Topical Guide to find the reference.

	1	2	3	4	5	6	7	8	9	10	11	12	13	14	15	16	17	18	19	20
A	T	B	I	L	O	T	B	H	R	I	D	E	Z	C	L	E	O	B	O	Z
B	I	R	A	D	N	R	A	M	M	O	B	O	A	N	O	U	N	N	U	N
C	N	O	D	S	R	W	A	X	H	E	S	N	O	R	Y	I	P	O	S	E
D	P	D	O	R	C	G	U	S	L	O	P	W	S	A	R	H	O	A	U	R
E	T	K	N	P	N	I	P	N	S	A	L	I	L	L	Y	L	P	B	U	T
F	T	R	Q	W	X	A	Z	H	E	A	O	N	A	R	Y	E	R	Z	O	D
G	B	O	W	D	N	B	O	C	O	N	T	U	N	W	H	T	S	A	T	A
H	I	C	O	S	O	N	A	Y	Y	V	E	V	T	H	O	X	R	A	N	V
I	L	E	L	N	D	N	U	L	N	N	U	B	O	A	R	I	P	R	R	A
J	A	H	Z	O	B	N	M	O	R	I	V	S	P	E	N	A	K	E	Y	L

D&C ____ : ____

Blackout Clues: E12, G13, I5, H5, E4, I15, C17, B20, F17, G16, H13, I14, J16, E7, D11 E5, D6, I20, G1, D5, J20, A17, C4, D3, H15, G4, A16, E17, F3, D1, J3, D20, E2, I8, J13, H17, F19, D15, D19, B17, F13, H6, I7, J15, C11, C16, E14, G9, F5, F11, I16, C18, D14, B13, J11, A9, C8, D7, G3, H10, J1, I3, B3, A20, D13, F2, H16, E3, H2, J2, C19, G8, A4, G6, I18, E16, I4, D17, J6, F7, A14, E13, G20, J19, A1, C2, C1, J5, G12, G17, A2, I1, I10, J17, A10, B1, H12, A13, B5, D8, J8, I9, A7, J18, A5, B6, D9, E8, H3, E11, A18, C7, B8, C5, A11, G10, B14, B12, D4, F6, F10, I11, J9, B10, E20, B19, C14, I12, F18, H19, F14, C13

Lesson 28	Trials Strengthen Faith

PREPARATION: Lesson 28 and enrichment activity 2 (p. 157) in the Primary 5 D&C/Church History manual.

ACTIVITY:
Premortal Life/Earth Life Quiz

Show images and answer questions: *Where did we come from?* (show premortal life circle.) • Heaven was our first estate (show plastic spirit). There we passed a test to come to earth and receive a physical body.

What test did we pass to come to earth? • We chose to follow Jesus and keep all of Heavenly Father's commandments (place plastic spirit over body and place on earth circle.) Our spirit was given a chance to come to earth to live in a body to be tested. *What do we need to do to pass the earth life test?* • If we keep the commandments we will have passed the test and can receive our reward (read Abraham 3:26), to live with Heavenly Father and Jesus again (in the second-estate earth circle, write what you will do.)

TO MAKE: Copy, color, and cut out the visuals that follow for each child on cardstock paper. Cut out a plastic spirit with head on fold-line of a plastic sheet protector to slide over doll's head.

SCRIPTURE CHALLENGE: See p. 92, 106
THOUGHT TREAT (when appropriate): Gingerbread Boy/Girl.

Lesson 29	Share the Gospel of Jesus Christ

PREPARATION: Lesson 29 and enrichment activity 2 (p. 164) in the Primary 5 D&C/Church History manual.

ACTIVITY: Missionary-Stretch Chart

This will remind children that they can be a missionary now. Chart shows 10 ways they can stretch their talents as a missionary.
TO MAKE: Copy, color, and cut out the visuals for girl or boy. Glue parts together.

SCRIPTURE CHALLENGE: See p. 92, 107
THOUGHT TREAT (when appropriate): Stretch-Tall Licorice String. Give children a string of licorice, and as they eat, have them stretch it and talk about stretching their talents to serve as a missionary. Remind them to start now to increase their missionary skills and talents, so that when they have an opportunity to serve, they will be ready.

I CAN BE A MISSIONARY **NOW!** 10 WAYS TO STRETCH YOUR TALENTS AS A MISSIONARY!

• Learn the Articles of Faith

• Read the scriptures

• Be a friend to those left alone

GLUE TO SIDE A

• Read the Church magazines

• Be courteous and kind

• Learn the Church hymns

• Share my testimony of Jesus

• Be a good example to others

• Share a Church video with a friend

• Invite friends to Church activities

I CAN BE A MISSIONARY NOW!

10 WAYS TO STRETCH YOUR TALENTS AS A MISSIONARY!

• Learn the Articles of Faith

• Read the scriptures

• Be a friend to those left alone

GLUE TO SIDE A

• Read the Church magazines

• Be courteous and kind

• Learn the Church hymns

• Share my testimony of Jesus

• Be a good example to others

• Share a Church video with a friend

• Invite friends to Church activities

Lesson 30   Prepare to Meet Jesus at Second Coming

PREPARATION: Review Lesson 30 and enrichment activity 1 (p. 170) in the Primary 5 D&C/Church History manual.

ACTIVITY: Strong Heart Mobile

This mobile shows children ways they can be strong. It reminds them that if their thoughts are centered around Jesus Christ, and if they keep Him in their heart at all times, they will be ready when He comes again.

TO MAKE: Copy, color, and cut out the visual that follows for each child. Note: Copy mobile using two different colors so one side is one color and other side is another color. To assemble: Lay the "My ♥ (heart) will not . . ." side face down with the pieces ½-inch apart. Place a 2-inch string down the center and tape to strips (still ½-inch apart). Glue second set of heart strips to the first set of heart strips (that are face down). Parts move left and right. Hang mobile.

SCRIPTURE CHALLENGE: See p. 92, 107

THOUGHT TREAT (when appropriate): Heart-Shaped Candy (cinnamon hearts or gummy hearts). Tell children, "If your heart is honest in wanting to keep the commandments, you will find a peaceful warm feeling in your heart."

Lesson 31   Prophet Guides as We Listen

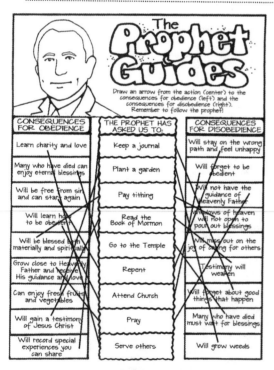

PREPARATION: Review Lesson 31 and enrichment activity 2 (p. 178) in the Primary 5 D&C/Church History manual.

ACTIVITY: Choices-and-Consequences Crossmatch

This puzzle helps children realize the good and bad consequences that come from choosing to listen to or reject the words of the living prophet. To do crossmatch, draw an arrow from the action the prophet has asked us to do (in the center) to the left to show the consequences for obedience and to the right to show consequences for disobedience.

Answer Key: **ACROSS:** 5—Heavenly Father, 7—ask, 8—morning, 9—listen, 10—thank, 15—still small voice, 17—help **DOWN:** 1—Holy Ghost, 2—prayer, 3—Jesus Christ, 4—yes, 6—guidance, 11—knees, 12—night, 13—blessings, 14—no, 18—peace.

TO MAKE: Copy, color, and cut out crossmatch.

SCRIPTURE CHALLENGE: See p. 92, 108

THOUGHT TREAT (when appropriate): Prophet-Speaks-and-I-Listen Cookie Crunch. Children can crunch on a cookie as you read the prophet's message.

My ♥ will not fail me. I will be prepared for Jesus' coming!

D&C 45:26

Repent and be baptized.

Stand ye in holy places.

Receive the truth.

Follow the Holy Spirit.

Do not be deceived.

Draw an arrow from the action (center) to the consequences for obedience (left) and the consequences for disobedience (right). Remember to follow the prophet!

CONSEQUENCES FOR OBEDIENCE	THE PROPHET HAS ASKED US TO:	CONSEQUENCES FOR DISOBEDIENCE
Learn charity and love	Keep a journal	Will stay on the wrong path and feel unhappy
Many who have died can enjoy eternal blessings	Plant a garden	Will forget to be obedient
Will be free from sin and can start again	Pay tithing	Will not have the guidance of Heavenly Father
Will learn how to be obedient	Read the Book of Mormon	Windows of heaven will not open to pour out blessings
Will be blessed both materially and spiritually	Go to the Temple	Will miss out on the joy of caring for others
Grow close to Heavenly Father and receive His guidance and love	Repent	Testimony will weaken
Can enjoy fresh fruits and vegetables	Attend Church	Will forget about good things that happen
Will gain a testimony of Jesus Christ	Pray	Many who have died must wait for blessings
Will record special experiences you can share	Serve others	Will grow weeds

Lesson 32   Faithfully Rely on Heavenly Father

PREPARATION: Review Lesson 32 and suggested home reading (p. 185) in the Primary 5 D&C/Church History manual.

ACTIVITY: Bite-size Memorize

Children can memorize this scripture to know that they can rely on Heavenly Father anytime. Faith and prayer are the keys to receiving guidance and making decisions. As children obey the commandments the Holy Ghost will guide them.

TO MAKE: Copy, color, and cut out the visual that follows for each child.

SCRIPTURE CHALLENGE: See p. 92, 108

THOUGHT TREAT (when appropriate): Seeds of Faith. Give children sunflower seeds in a cup or plastic bag. Tell them that faith is a little seed. It starts small and grows. The more we think good thoughts and pray to our Heavenly Father, the stronger our faith becomes.

Lesson 33   Work & Leave a Legacy of Love

PREPARATION: Review Lesson 33 and enrichment activity 5 (p. 191) in the Primary 5 D&C/Church History manual.

ACTIVITY: Pioneer Spirit Thank-you Card

Help children create a thank-you card they can give to a loved one to let them know that their hard work is appreciated. Encourage children to develop the pioneer spirit like the hard-working Saints who settled Nauvoo. Have them think of their parents and grandparents who have left their legacy of love, and the pioneers who unselfishly took on heavy burdens to bring us what we have today. Encourage children to work hard at righteous goals so they will prosper and leave a legacy of love for their children and loved ones.

TO MAKE: Copy, color, and cut out the visual that follows for each child on cardstock paper. Sign card and deliver or mail.

SCRIPTURE CHALLENGE: See p. 92, 109

THOUGHT TREAT (when appropriate): Pioneer Peanut-Butter Sandwich. Tell children, "The pioneers stuck to their beliefs just like this peanut butter sticks to this sandwich or the roof of your mouth. We too can stick to our beliefs."

Peace be unto thy soul; thine adversity and thine afflictions shall be but a small moment; And then, if thou endure it well, God shall exhalt thee on high; thou shalt triumph over all thy foes.

D&C 121:7-8

...Here's a THANKS from me!

Your hard work is appreciated!

You're such a buzzzzy bee.....

Lesson 34   Baptisms for the Dead

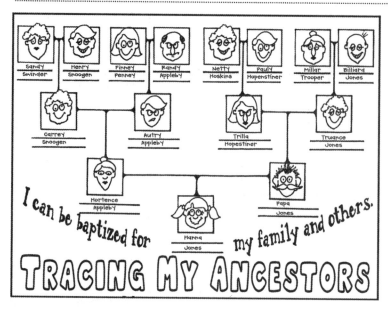

I can be baptized for my family and others.

TRACING MY ANCESTORS

PREPARATION: Review Lesson 34 and enrichment activity 4 (p. 197) in the Primary 5 D&C/Church History manual.

ACTIVITY: Tracing My Ancestors Pedigree Chart

Children can trace their ancestors on this fun three-generations chart. Tell children, The Prophet Joseph Smith said, "The greatest responsibility in this world that God has laid upon us is to seek after our dead." (Teachings of the Prophet Joseph Smith, p. 356, compiled by Joseph Fielding Smith.) We can submit names to the temple for this important work, to link/seal children to their parents together forever.

To Create Chart: (1) Write in the names of each ancestor to complete the family group chart.

(2) Hold the pedigree chart to the window with hair and facial features behind chart. With light shining through, create each ancestor by tracing hair and facial features into each box (starting with your own family).

TO MAKE: Copy, color, and cut out the visuals that follow for each child. See details above.

SCRIPTURE CHALLENGE: See p. 92, 109

THOUGHT TREAT (when appropriate): Graham Crackers and Milk. As children dip their graham crackers in milk, have them name an ancestor for each cracker segment eaten.

Lesson 35   Living Worthy for Temple Blessings

I love to see the temple.

I'm going there someday!

PREPARATION: Review Lesson 35 and enrichment activity 1 (p. 202-203) and testimony (p. 203) in the Primary 5 D&C/Church History manual.

ACTIVITY: Temple Photo Frame

This frame reminds children to live worthy of temple blessings.

TO MAKE: Copy, color, and cut out the visual that follows for each child on cardstock paper. Cut out inside of frame back. Cut out flap in back of frame and fold to stand frame up. Ask child to place photo next to temple and glue frame sides to back of frame.

SCRIPTURE CHALLENGE: See p. 92, 110

THOUGHT TREAT (when appropriate): Temple Mints. Hand out temple-shaped mints or mints and tell children that Heavenly Father "mint" (meant) for all of us to share the blessings of the temple.

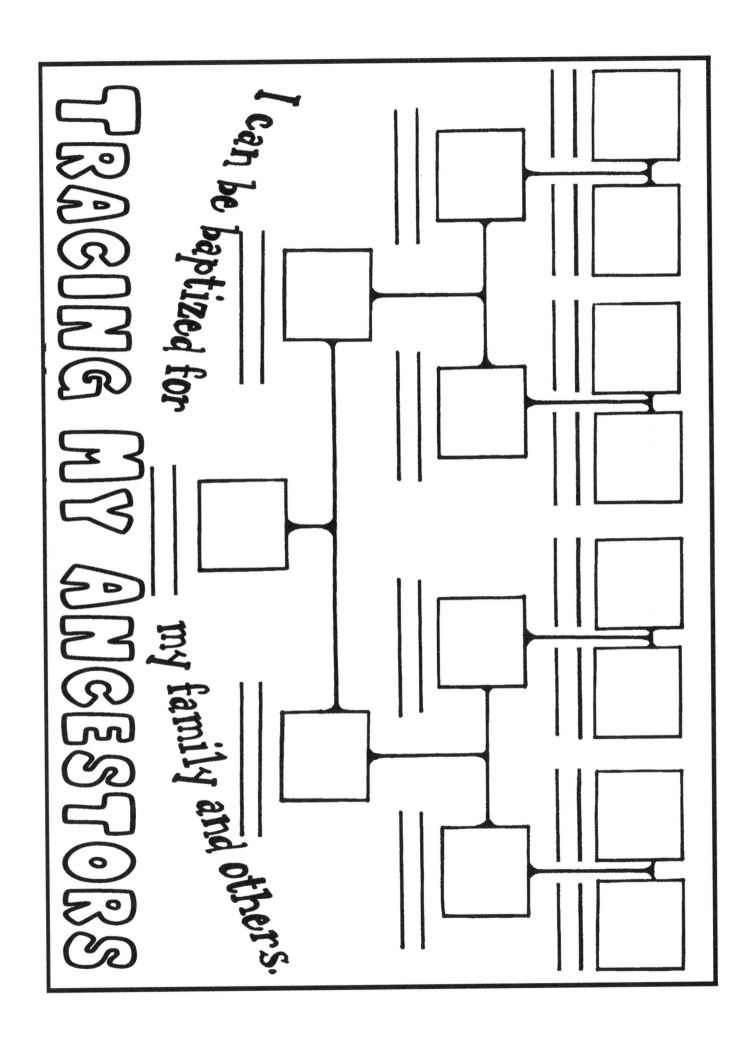

TRACING MY ANCESTORS

I can be baptized for my family and others.

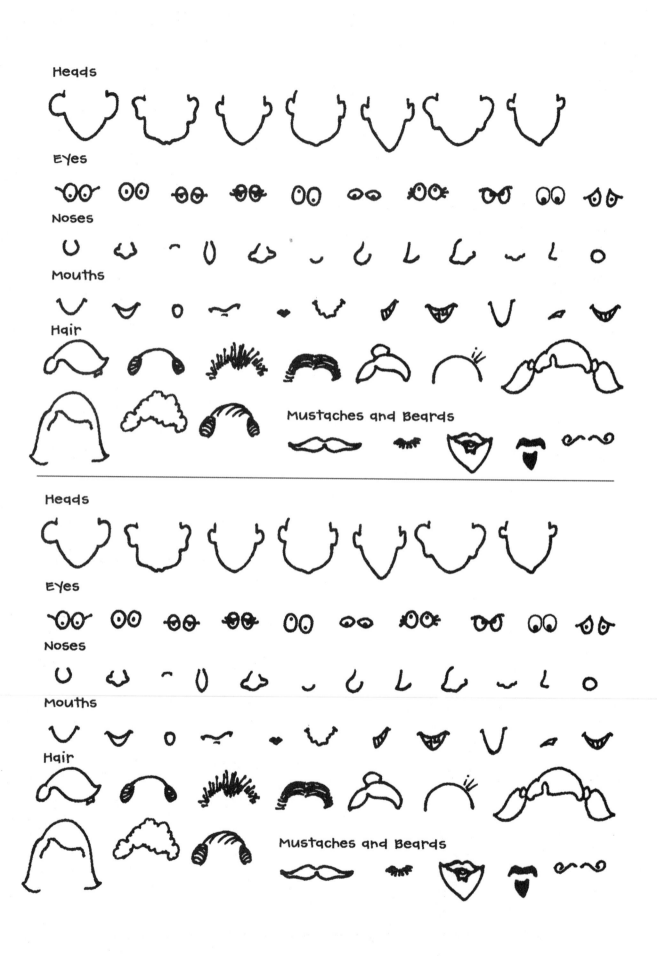

I love to see the temple.

cut out

I'm going there someday!

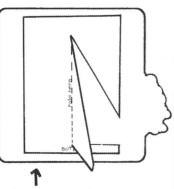

Attach stand to back of frame using glue or tape as shown.

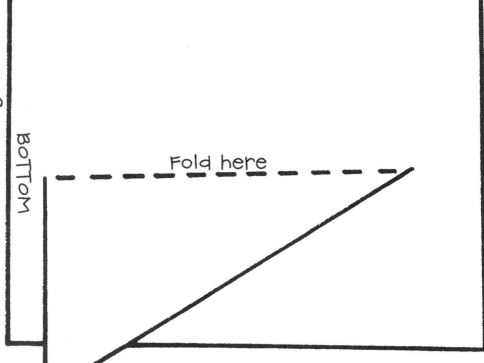

BOTTOM

Fold here

Lesson 36   Articles of Faith Strengthen Testimony

PREPARATION: Review Lesson 36 and enrichment activities 5 and 6 (p. 207) in the Primary 5 D&C/Church History manual.

ACTIVITY:
13 Lucky Numbers Game

Play the Lucky Numbers Game to learn the keywords and learn the Articles of Faith.

To Play: Divide players into two teams. Place a marker for each team at START. The first team rolls the die or chooses a 1-5 slip of paper and moves that number of spaces on the board. The team then looks at the number under the marker and reads the keyword that matches the number. The players can recite that Article of Faith to earn 20 points for their team. The first team to get to FINISH, or to earn 100 points by saying their Articles of Faith, wins.

TO MAKE: Copy, color, and cut out the game board follows. You will need two different coins (markers), and a die. Instead of using a die, you may write the numbers 1–5 on separate strips of paper to draw from a container to determine moves (make several sets of numbers 1–5). Make a game for children to take home.

SCRIPTURE CHALLENGE: See p. 92, 110

THOUGHT TREAT (when appropriate): Lucky-13 Cookies. Write numbers 1-13 on 13 different sugar cookies using frosting in a tube. As each child eat's their numbered cookie, have them recite the Article of Faith that belongs to that number. Gift idea: Give children an Articles of Faith card or a large Articles of Faith poster (available at LDS bookstores or the Church Distribution Center).

More Articles of Faith Learning Games:

To play games 1 and 2 below, make two copies of the Lucky Numbers Game board that follows and cut up number/word squares to make two sets. Choose from the following activities to help children learn numbers (ages 3-5) and keywords (ages 6-teens).

GAME 1—Lucky 13 Number/Keyword Match Game. This game helps children learn the keywords that go with each number. (1) Turn numbers facedown and divide children into two teams. (2) Take turns turning numbers over to make a match. Older team members can help younger children make their match. After all matches are made, the team with the most matches wins!

GAME 2—Articles of Faith Keyword Toss-and-Tell. This game helps children recite the Articles of Faith that match with the keywords. (1) With children in a circle and number/word squares in a bowl in the center, have one person toss the squares into the air. (2) Divide children into two teams, then have them rush to grab the squares. (3) Have team members gather their matches. (4) Children ask the other team for the number/word square they need by saying the Article of Faith that matches the square needed. If they say it correctly with the help of their team, they can take the square from the other team. Keep playing until all squares are matched. If both teams cannot say the Article of Faith, look it up and read it aloud. The unknown squares must be placed in a pile in the center. The team with the most matches win.

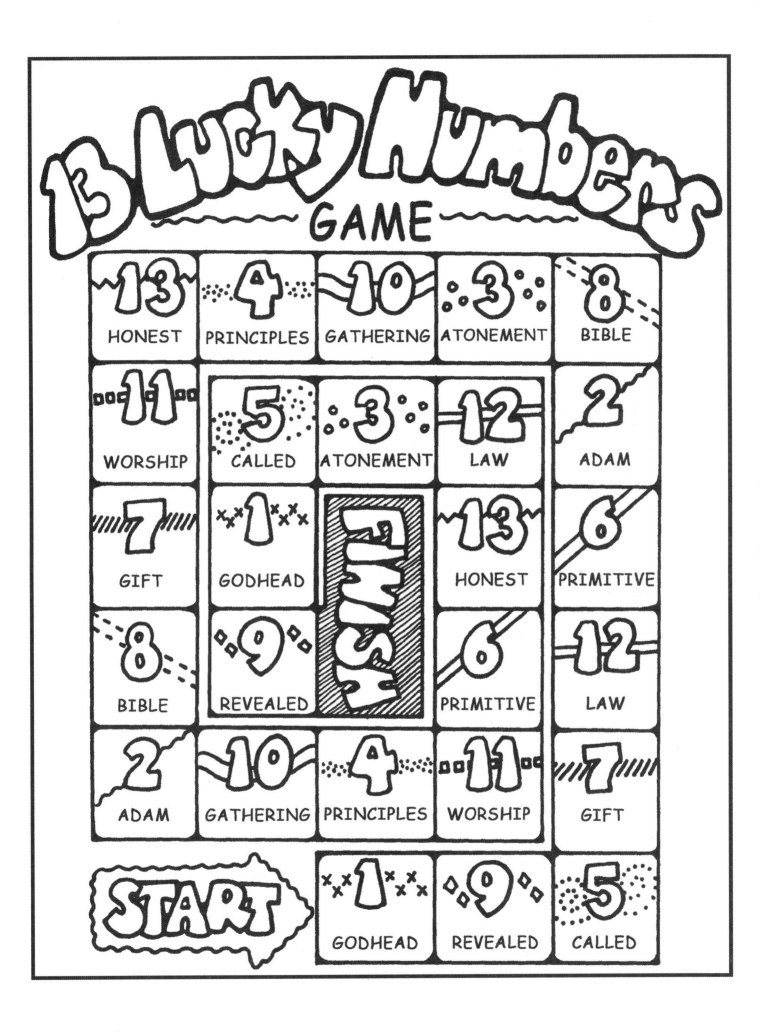

Lesson 37   Prophet Joseph Smith Restored Jesus' Gospel

Joseph Smith

God's Chosen Prophet

• Look up the scripture below and find the words that will fill in the blanks.

D&C 135:3

Joseph Smith, the <u>Prophet</u> and <u>Seer</u> of the Lord, has done more, save Jesus only, for the <u>salvation</u> of men in this <u>world</u>, than any other <u>man</u> that ever lived in it. In the short space of <u>twenty</u> years, he has brought forth the <u>Book</u> of <u>Mormon</u> which he <u>translated</u> by the gift and <u>power</u> of God, and has been the means of <u>publishing</u> it on <u>two</u> continents; has sent the <u>fulness</u> of the everlasting <u>gospel</u>, which it contained, to the <u>four</u> quarters of the <u>earth</u>; has brought forth the <u>revelations</u> and <u>Commandments</u> which compose this book of <u>Doctrine</u> and <u>Covenants</u>, and many other <u>wise</u> documents and <u>instructions</u> for the <u>benefit</u> of the <u>children</u> of men; <u>gathered</u> many <u>thousands</u> of the Latter-day Saints, founded a great <u>city</u>, and left a fame and <u>name</u>, that cannot be <u>slain</u>. He lived <u>great</u>, and he died <u>great</u> in the <u>eyes</u> of God and his people; and like most of the Lord's <u>anointed</u> in <u>ancient</u> times, has <u>sealed</u> his <u>mission</u> and his works with his own <u>blood</u>.

Review Lesson 37 and enrichment activities 2 and 4 (p. 214-215) in the Primary 5 D&C/Church History manual.

ACTIVITY: Tribute Search

Tell children the following: "John Taylor made a statement about Joseph Smith to remind us of the Prophet Joseph's achievements written in D&C 135:3." Children can search this lengthy scripture to fill in the blanks and learn of the Prophet's great service to us and to the Church. On the worksheet there are some achievements missing. Ask children to fill in the blanks to complete the scripture. Encourage children to tape this tribute to their wall next to their bed, reminding them of the achievements of this great man.

TO MAKE: Copy, color, and cut out the visual that follows for each child.

SCRIPTURE CHALLENGE: See p. 92, 111

THOUGHT TREAT (when appropriate): Sparkling Juice. Share with children some sparkling apple juice or orange juice (mix 7-up or other clear soda pop with juice). Tell children that just as this sparkling soda pop adds flavor to the juice, we too can add flavor to our testimonies by adding the sparkling example of Joseph Smith to our list of heroes.

Lesson 38   The Prophet Today Leads Us

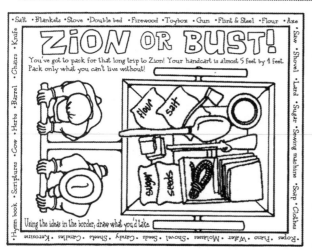

• Salt • Blankets • Stove • Double bed • Firewood • Toybox • Gun • Flint & Steel • Flour • Axe

ZION OR BUST!

You've got to pack for that long trip to Zion! Your handcart is almost 5 feet by 4 feet. Pack only what you can't live without!

Using the ideas in the border, draw what you'd take.

Flour Salt Sugar seeds

• Hymn book • Scriptures • Cow • Herbs • Barrel • Chairs • Knife

• Saw • Shovel • Lard • Sugar • Sewing machine • Soap • Clothes

• Ropes • Piano • Water • Molasses • Shovel • Seeds • Sheets • Candy • Candles • Kerosine

PREPARATION: Review Lesson 38 and enrichment activity 2 (p. 220) in the Primary 5 D&C/Church History manual.

ACTIVITY: Zion or Bust! Handcart Checklist

Help children think ahead, just as the Mormon pioneers had to measure and plan what they would take in their 4' x 5' handcart. The pioneers were led by Brigham Young to the Salt Lake Valley. Choose from the items written in the border, and draw inside and outside the handcart what each child would take to Zion.

TO MAKE: Copy, color, and cut out the visual that follows for each child.

SCRIPTURE CHALLENGE: See p. 92, 111

THOUGHT TREAT (when appropriate): Hit-the-Trail Treats. Let children try dried fruits, vegetables, or jerky, and remind them that these foods were taken along the pioneer trail.

Joseph Smith
God's Chosen Prophet

• Look up the scripture below and find the words that will fill in the blanks.

—— D&C 135:3 ——

Joseph Smith, the _____ and _____ of the Lord, has done more, save Jesus only, for the _____ of men in this _____, than any other _____ that ever lived in it. In the short space of _____ years, he has brought forth the _____ of _____, which he _____ by the _____ and _____ of God, and has been the means of _____ it on _____ continents; has sent the _____ of the everlasting _____, which it contained, to the _____ quarters of the _____; has brought forth the _____ and _____ which compose this book of _____ and _____, and many other _____ documents and _____ for the _____ of the _____ of men; _____ many _____ of the Latter-day Saints, founded a great _____, and left a fame and _____ that cannot be _____. He lived _____, and he died _____ in the _____ of _____ and his people; and like most of the Lord's _____ in _____ times, has _____ his _____ and his works with his own _____.

ZION OR BUST!

You've got to pack for that long trip to Zion! Your handcart is almost 5 feet by 4 feet. Pack only what you can't live without!

Using the ideas in the border, draw what you'd take.

•Hymn book •Scriptures •Cow •Herbs •Barrel •Chairs •Knife •Salt •Blankets •Stove •Double bed •Firewood •Toybox •Gun •Flint & Steel •Flour •Axe •Saw •Shovel •Lard •Sugar •Sewing machine •Soap •Clothes •Ropes •Piano •Water •Molasses •Shovel •Seeds •Candy •Sheets •Candles •Kerosine

Lesson 39	Service Brings Happiness

PREPARATION: Review Lesson 39 and enrichment activity 3 (p. 227) in the Primary 5 D&C/Church History manual.

ACTIVITY: Service-station Sack of Reminders

Encourage children to take this bag home and pull out acts of kindness each day/week to remind them to serve others. Talk about the rewards that come from service (e.g. making one feel happy, increasing talents, and the blessings that come from Heavenly Father). Encourage children to add to these deeds by making their own list of service ideas.

TO MAKE: Copy, color, and cut out the visual that follows for each child. Glue label on a brown paper lunch-size bag. Place wordstrips in the bag.

SCRIPTURE CHALLENGE: See p. 92, 112

THOUGHT TREAT (when appropriate): Life Savers Candy Cars. Give each child a whole pack of Life Savers candies (for the car body), and glue individual Life Savers on sides for the wheel. Remind children that if they speed by others not stopping to serve, they could swerve off the straight and narrow path that leads back to our Heavenly Father.

Lesson 40	Work Hard to Serve Like the Pioneers

PREPARATION: Review Lesson 40 (p. 229-236) in the Primary 5 D&C/Church History manual.

ACTIVITY: Pioneer Word-find Puzzle

Fill in puzzle blanks using the words below to think about the struggles of the Mormon pioneers who found and settled the Salt Lake valley. Cross out or highlight words as you add them to the trail of words. Remind children that the pioneers prepared the way for thousands of others to come. Their hardships and hard work are described in this puzzle. Do puzzle individually or as teams. The first to finish wins.

TO MAKE: Copy, color, and cut out the visual for each child.

SCRIPTURE CHALLENGE: See p. 92, 112

THOUGHT TREAT (when appropriate): "Grape-ful" Grapes. Share grapes as you talk about how grateful you are for the pioneers' hard work. The pioneers pulled covered wagons across the plains, built a new trail called the Mormon trail, protected themselves from Indian attacks, made friends with many Indians, fished and hunted for food, crossed large rivers and streams, traveled with horses and oxen over the rough Rocky Mountains, and planted food along the way, preparing the way for thousands of Saints to enter the Salt Lake Valley.

You're at the
SERVICE STATION!
Gas up, take off, and
help those you "car" about.

Read a story to sister or brother.	Rake leaves, but not in trees.
Make someone's bed.	Do housework happily.
Fix a snack, add a note, and deliver.	Fix breakfast for Mom or Dad.
Vacuum with vigor for 10 minutes.	Ask your family how you can help.
Use a broom to clean cobwebs from high places.	Be a dust buster by polishing the furniture.
Set the table because you're able.	Pick out a recipe and cook up a storm (great food)!
Visit and cheer up the elderly.	Make a vegetable snack for dinner.
Make a homemade gift and deliver.	Compliment someone by saying "cool _____," or "great _____."
Make, eat, and clean up after a snack.	Take a treat to someone on your street.
Ask a friend how you can help, and do it.	Clean your room without being asked.
Clean up your own messes.	Empty the garbage and recycle bin.
Wipe mirrors with window cleaner.	Fold and put away your own laundry.
Be a dirt detective (sweep the floor).	Wash the dishes.

I feel GRATEFUL for the PIONEERS

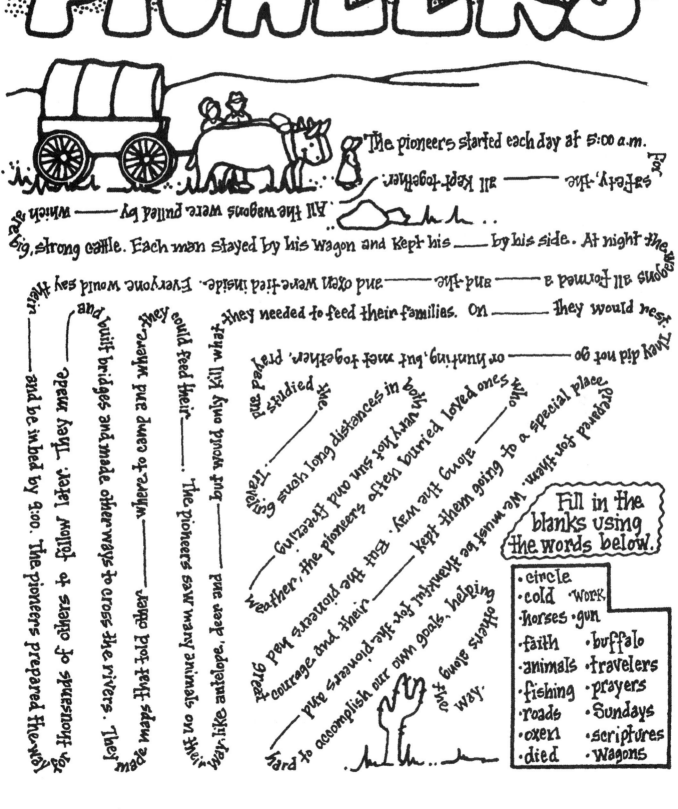

The pioneers started each day at 5:00 a.m. For safety, the _____ all kept together. _____ which are big, strong cattle. Each man stayed by his wagon and kept his _____ by his side. At night the wagons all formed a _____ and the _____ and oxen were tied inside. Everyone would say their _____ they needed to feed their families. On _____ they would rest. They did not go _____ or hunting, but met together, prayed and studied the _____. Traveling such long distances in both very hot sun and freezing weather, the pioneers often buried loved ones who _____ along the way. But the pioneers had great courage and their _____ kept them going to a special place _____ prepared for them. We must be thankful for the pioneers and work hard to accomplish our own goals, helping others along the way.

All the wagons were pulled by _____. They needed to feed their families.

and be in bed by 9:00. The pioneers prepared the way for thousands of others to follow later. They made new _____ made maps that told other _____ where to camp and where they could feed their _____. The pioneers saw many animals on their way, like antelope, deer and _____ but would only kill what _____ and built bridges and made other ways to cross the rivers. They _____

Fill in the blanks using the words below.

- circle
- cold · work
- horses · gun
- faith · buffalo
- animals · travelers
- fishing · prayers
- roads · Sundays
- oxen · scriptures
- died · wagons

Lesson 41 — Keep the Sabbath Day Holy

PREPARATION: Review Lesson 41 and enrichment activity 1 (p. 242) in the Primary 5 D&C/Church History manual.

ACTIVITY:
Sabbath-day Decisions Drama-or-draw

Help children learn the difference between right and wrong Sabbath Day activities.

DECISION DRAMA-OR-DRAW: Children can play this game by dividing into teams, with opposing teams sitting across from one another. Children take turns drawing a wordstrip from a jar and reading it silently.

OPTION 1—DRAMA: Act out the activity.

OPTION 2—DRAW: Draw activity on paper or the chalkboard for all to see.

The first team to guess the activity and vote "yes" (good Sabbath activity) or vote "no" (not a good Sabbath activity) wins a point for their team. Play by voting on all wordstrips or until time runs out.

TO MAKE: Copy, color, and cut out the label and wordstrips that follow for each child. Mount label on a jar and place wordstrips inside.

SCRIPTURE CHALLENGE: See p. 92, 113

THOUGHT TREAT (when appropriate): Sabbath-day Hugs and Kisses. Purchase some Hershey's Hugs and Kisses chocolate candies. As you play the game (above), give out candies. Tell children that we show love (hugs/kisses) to Heavenly Father as we keep the Sabbath day holy.

Lesson 42 — Faith in Jesus Christ Helps Me

If ye will have faith in me ye shall have power to do whatsoever thing is expedient in me.
~Moroni 7:33

PREPARATION: Review Lesson 42 and enrichment activity 3 (p. 252) in the Primary 5 D&C/Church History manual.

ACTIVITY:
"Jesus Lights up My Life" Light-switch Cover

Remind children with this light-switch cover that Jesus Christ lit the way for pioneers to help them solve problems, and He can light the way for us to solve our problems in these latter-days. Ask children to place the cover over their light switch to remind them to have faith in Jesus Christ, and believe that He will help them with their problems.

TO MAKE: Copy, color, and cut out the visual that follows for each child on cardstock paper. Cut out the center to place over light switch.

SCRIPTURE CHALLENGE: See p. 92, 113

THOUGHT TREAT (when appropriate): Faith Finger Treats. Give each child five olives to place on their fingers. Before eating each olive, have them name a way they can increase faith in Jesus, e.g., pray, read scriptures, attend church, pay tithing, and listen in testimony meeting.

Shop for groceries . . . . no	Watch Church videos . . . . yes
Write to a missionary . . . . yes	Read Church magazines . . . . yes
Write letters . . . . yes	Read scripture stories . . . . yes
Visit the sick . . . . yes	Put on a scripture skit or play . . . yes
Go skiing . . . . no	Mop the floor . . . . no
Ride your bike . . . . no	Read brother or sister a story . . yes
Play with friends . . . . no	Listen to spiritual music . . . . yes
Pay your tithing . . . . yes	Help prepare a meal . . . . yes
Go to church . . . . yes	Read a book the prophet wrote . . yes
Visit with family . . . . yes	Play games with the family . . . . . yes
Have a family get-together . . . . yes	Have family prayer . . . . yes
Read the scriptures . . . . yes	Color a picture . . . . yes
Have family home evening . . . . . yes	Make a craft . . . . yes
Do the dishes . . . . yes	Write in your journal . . . . yes
Deep-clean the house . . . . no	Take notes in church . . . . yes
Mow the lawn . . . . no	Listen to your teacher . . . . yes
Clean the garage . . . . no	Participate in Primary . . . . yes
Wash the car . . . . no	Sit reverently in church . . . . yes
Go sun-tanning . . . . no	Visit grandparents . . . . yes
Go swimming . . . . no	Invite a friend to church . . . . yes
Eat out at a restaurant . . . . no	Do a kind deed . . . . yes
Make a card for someone . . . . . . yes	Make friends with the elderly . . . yes
Make your bed . . . . yes	Talk to your brother or sister . . . yes
Play the piano . . . . yes	Go for a short walk . . . . yes
Sing . . . . yes	Take a nap . . . . yes
Go fishing . . . . no	Bake cookies . . . . yes
Play sports . . . . no	Help set the table . . . . yes

Lesson 43   Valiantly Live the Gospel of Jesus Christ

PREPARATION: Review Lesson 43 and enrichment activity 5 (page 260) in the Primary 5 D&C/Church History manual.

ACTIVITY: Valiant Poster

Encourage children to color and post this poster that reminds them to live the gospel of Jesus Christ valiantly. "Valiant" describes both the handcart companies who came into the Salt Lake Valley, and us today as we keep the commandments and endure to the end. We can be valiant by being courageous, obedient, loving, kind, loyal, strong, true, faithful, honest, unselfish, patient, righteous, and forgiving.

TO MAKE: Copy, color, and cut out visual that follows for each child.

SCRIPTURE CHALLENGE: See p. 92, 114

THOUGHT TREAT (when appropriate): Valiant Vegetables. Give each child a few fresh, raw vegetables, (carrots, celery, broccoli, etc). Provide a ranch dressing to dip them in. As you munch, talk about the valiant pioneers who planted crops for those who would follow. They had the pioneer spirit of leaving behind something of value. Ask children what they would like to leave behind to prove that they are valiant.

Lesson 44   Living the Law of Chastity

PREPARATION: Review Lesson 44 and enrichment activity 2 (p. 269) and activity 6 (p. 271) in the Primary 5 D&C/Church History manual.

ACTIVITY: Temple-light Poster

As a reminder to live the law of chastity, children can punch pin holes in this backwards picture. When they place it in the window (facing out) they can see the message written forward on the other side as the light shines through the pin hole dots.

TO MAKE: Copy, color, and cut out the visual that follows for each child on cardstock paper. See directions above.

SCRIPTURE CHALLENGE: See p. 92, 114

THOUGHT TREAT (when appropriate): Temple-worthy Waffles. Precook frozen waffles, then butter and sprinkle cinnamon and sugar on top). Tell children that the waffles represent the strait and narrow paths we take to get to the temple. When we slip off the path (into the waffle hole) by doing something wrong, we need to repent and promise not to do the wrong action again. We can then get back on the path and keep the commandments so we are worthy to go to the temple when the time comes.

I will live VALIANTLY the gospel of Jesus Christ.

Lesson 45   Tithing Helps Build Up the Kingdom of God

PREPARATION: Review Lesson 45 and enrichment activity 2 (page 277) in the Primary 5 D&C/Church History manual.

ACTIVITY: Origami Tithing Purse/Wallet

Fold a tithing purse/wallet to hold tithing donations until child has the opportunity to pay. This purse/wallet can be placed in their scriptures for safekeeping. Children can store their tithing money here until they can pay it on Sunday. This will remind them that they will be blessed both spiritually and materially when they pay a full tithe.

TO MAKE: Copy, color, and cut out the visuals that follow for each child on cardstock paper. To fold, follow the instructions found on the pattern.

SCRIPTURE CHALLENGE: See p. 92, 115

THOUGHT TREAT (when appropriate): 1/10th Cupcake. Bake a cupcake for each child and one for the bishop. Give each child 10 M&M pieces of candy. Each child places one candy on the bishop's cupcake and nine on their cupcake. Deliver cupcake with donations to the bishop.

Lesson 46   Study and Prayer Strengthen Testimony

PREPARATION: Review Lesson 46 and enrichment activity 2 (p. 284) in the Primary 5 D&C/Church History manual.

ACTIVITY: Testimony Word Race

Race to find words that branch off from the word TESTIMONY. (1) Divide children into two teams with players sitting on chairs back to back. (2) Each player has pencil and TESTIMONY WORD RACE! chart in hand. Then begin. (3) Use the letters in TESTIMONY to inspire other words that connect. Words can be written in any direction—left, right, up, down, or diagonal. (4) Once a word is written, other words can branch off the words written. All words must be words that are part of the gospel of Jesus Christ, words that help strengthen testimony. (5) Children can earn 10 points for every word that branches off from the word TESTIMONY. (6) Children can earn 1 point for all words written after the first word that branches off from the word TESTIMONY. See chart on this page if you run out ideas. When time is up, team with the most connecting words wins.

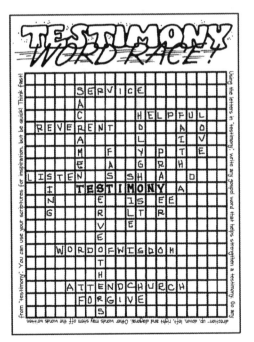

TO MAKE: Copy, color, and cut out the visual that follows for each child.

SCRIPTURE CHALLENGE: See p. 92, 115

THOUGHT TREAT (when appropriate): TESTIMONY Treats. Give children food that begins with letters in TESTIMONY, i.e.: taffy, egg, saltine cracker, toast, icing, melon, orange, nuts, yogurt.

A. Fold in half with illustrations on the outside.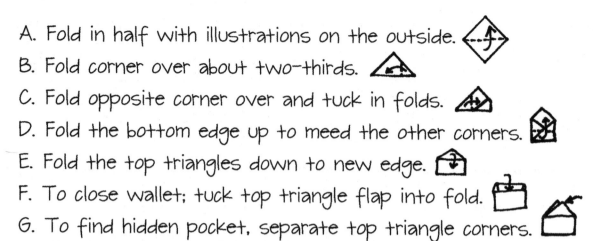

B. Fold corner over about two-thirds.

C. Fold opposite corner over and tuck in folds.

D. Fold the bottom edge up to meed the other corners.

E. Fold the top triangles down to new edge.

F. To close wallet; tuck top triangle flap into fold.

G. To find hidden pocket, separate top triangle corners.

I want to give my 10%
when I pay my tithing
spiritually and materially
I will be blessed both

TESTIMONY WORD RACE!

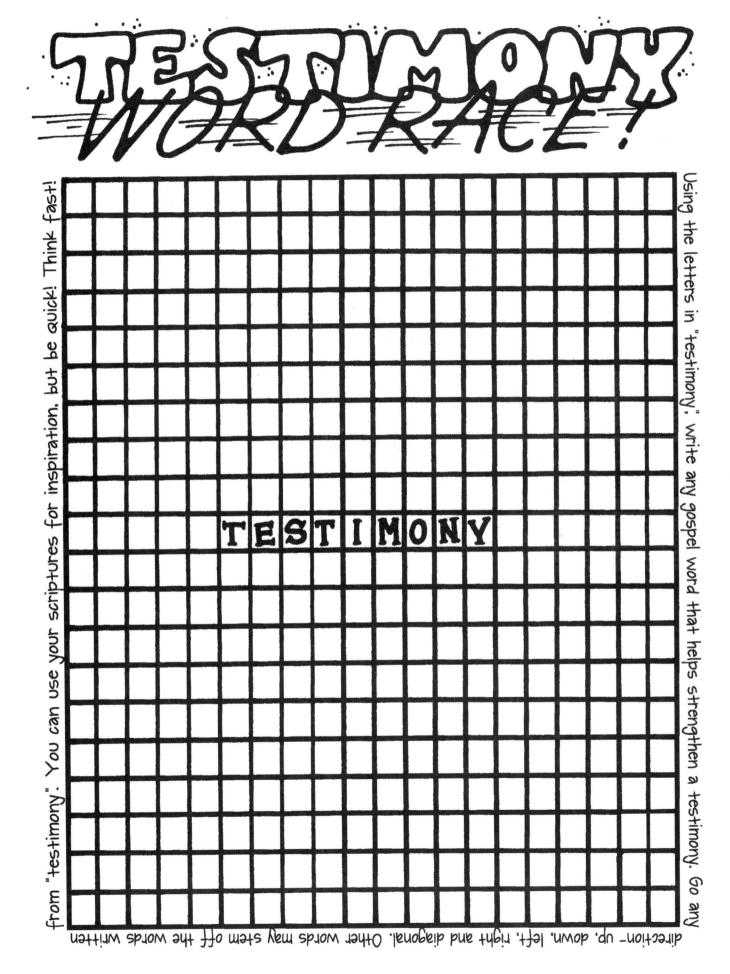

TESTIMONY

Using the letters in "testimony," write any gospel word that helps strengthen a testimony. Go any direction— up, down, left, right and diagonal. Other words may stem off the words written from "testimony." You can use your scriptures for inspiration, but be quick! Think fast!

My Scripture Challenge Cards

Book Belongs To:

_____

_____

Scripture Challenge:

Every week when a lesson is given,
study the scripture CARD featured for that lesson.

Then fill in the blanks and color the image to
show that your testimony is growing.

Remember the Book of Mormon Promise:
Moroni 10:4-5

And when ye shall receive these things, I would exhort you that ye would ask
God, the Eternal Father, in the name of Christ, if these things are not true;
and if ye shall ask with a sincere heart, with real intent, having faith in Christ,
he will manifest the truth of it unto you, by the power of the Holy Ghost.

#1   First Vision:

Joseph Smith Saw Heavenly Father and Jesus

Search & Ponder Challenge:
Read Joseph Smith—History 1:1-20

Joseph Smith—History 1:18-19

"No sooner, therefore, did I get possession of

myself, so as to be able to speak, than

I asked the Personages who ___ ___ ___ ___ ___ above

me in the light, which of all the sects was

___ ___ ___ ___ ___ (for . . . it had never entered into

my heart that ___ ___ ___ were wrong)--and which I

should join. I was answered that I must join

___ ___ ___ ___ of them."

#2   Apostasy:

Jesus Christ's Church Is Restored

Search & Ponder Challenge:
Read D&C 1:17-23

D&C 1:17-18, 21, 23

"I the Lord . . . called . . . upon my servant Joseph

Smith, Junior, and spake unto him from heaven, and

gave him commandments; And also gave

commandments to others that they should proclaim

. . . unto the world; . . . That ___ ___ ___ ___ ___

also might increase in the earth; . . . That the

fulness of my ___ ___ ___ ___ ___ ___ might be proclaimed."

#3   Gospel Fulness:
Angel Moroni's Good News Message

Search & Ponder Challenge:
Read Joseph Smith—History 1:30-35

Joseph Smith—History 1:34-35
"He said there was a __ __ __ __ deposited, written upon __ __ __ __ __ __ __ __ __ __, giving an account of the former inhabitants of this continent, . . . that the fulness of the everlasting __ __ __ __ __ __ was contained in it, as delivered by the Savior to the ancient inhabitants . . . Also . . . the __ __ __ __ and Thummim [was] deposited with the plates."

#4   Prepare:
I Will Prepare to Serve Jesus and Others

Search & Ponder Challenge:
Read Joseph Smith—History 1:53-58

Joseph Smith—History 1:55
"As my father's worldly circumstances were very limited, we were under the necessity of __ __ __ __ __ __ __ __ with our hands, hiring out by day's __ __ __ __ and otherwise, as we could get opportunity . . . and by continuous __ __ __ __ __ were enabled to get a comfortable maintenance."

#5   Obedience:

Heavenly Father Will Help Me As I Obey

Search & Ponder Challenge:
Read Joseph Smith—History 1:59-60

Joseph Smith—History 1:59-60
"At length the time arrived for obtaining the plates . . . . The same heavenly messenger
_ _ _ _ _ _ _ _ _ _ _ them up to me with this charge: that I should be
_ _ _ _ _ _ _ _ _ _ _ _ _ _
for them; . . . [and] preserve them, until he, the messenger, should call for them."

#6   Prayer:

I Will Seek Heavenly Father's Guidance

Search & Ponder Challenge:
Read D&C 3:1-3 and 10:1-5

D&C 3:2
"For God doth not walk in _ _ _
_ _ _ _ paths, neither doth he
turn to the right hand nor to the left,
neither doth he vary from that which
he hath said, therefore his
_ _ _ _ _ _ are
_ _ _ _ _ _ _ _ _ _, and his
course is one _ _ _ _ _ _ _
round."

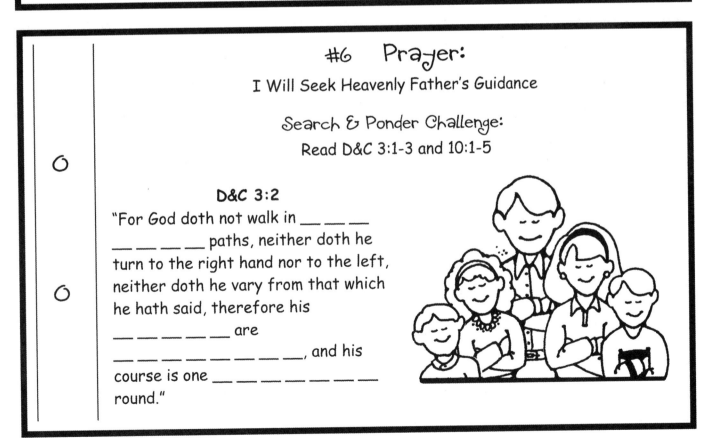

#7   Holy Ghost:

The Holy Ghost Will Guide and Comfort Me

Search & Ponder Challenge:
Read D&C 8:2-3

D&C 8:2-3

"Yea, behold, I will tell you in your __ __ __ __ and in your __ __ __ __ __, by the Holy Ghost, which shall come upon you and which shall dwell in your heart. Now, behold, this is the __ __ __ __ __ __ __ of revelation; behold, this is the spirit by which __ __ __ __ __ brought the children of Israel through the __ __ __ Sea on dry ground."

#8   Priesthood Blessings:

I Will Be Worthy to Receive Blessings

Search & Ponder Challenge:
Read D&C 13 (and heading)

D&C 13

"Upon you my fellow servants, in the name of Messiah I confer the

__ __ __ __ __ __ __ __ __ __ __ __ of Aaron, which holds the keys of the

ministering of __ __ __ __ __ __ __, and of the gospel of repentance, and of baptism by immersion for the remission of sins."

#9   Book of Mormon:

I Will Bear My Testimony of Truth

Search & Ponder Challenge:
Read D&C 17:1-4

D&C 17:1, 3

"You shall have a __ __ __ __ of the plates . . . and also the breastplate, the sword of Laban, the Urim and __ __ __ __ __ __ __ which were given to the brother of __ __ __ __ __ upon the mount, when he talked with the Lord face to face, and the miraculous directors which were given to __ __ __ __ . . . And . . . you shall testify of them by the power of __ __ __."

#10   Book of Mormon Publication:

I'm Grateful I Have It to Read and Study

Search & Ponder Challenge:
Read D&C 20:18-12 and
Book of Mormon Introduction

D&C 20:8-9, 11-12

"God . . . gave him [Joseph Smith] power . . . to __ __ __ __ __ __ __ __ __ __ the Book of Mormon; Which contains a record of a fallen people, and the fulness of the gospel of Jesus Christ . . . Proving . . . the holy scriptures are __ __ __ __, . . . showing that he is the same God yesterday, today, and __ __ __ __ __ __ __."

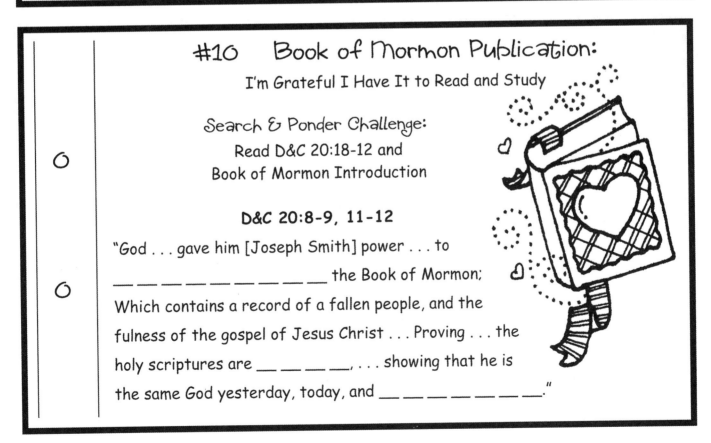

#11   Restoration:
The True Church Was Restored to the Earth

Search & Ponder Challenge:
Read D&C 20:1-4 and 21:1-5

D&C 115:4

"For thus shall my __ __ __ __ __ __ be called
in the last days, even The Church of
__ __ __ __ __ __   __ __ __ __ __ __ of
__ __ __ __ __ -day __ __ __ __ __ __."

#12   Ordinances Restored:
I'm Grateful to Be Baptized

Search & Ponder Challenge:
Read D&C 20:72-79 and 2 Nephi 31:17-21

D&C 20:37

"All those who __ __ __ __ __ __ themselves
before God, and desire to be baptized, and come
forth with __ __ __ __ __ __ __ hearts and
__ __ __ __ __ __ __ __ __ spirits, and . . . have
truly repented of all their sins, and are willing to
take upon them the __ __ __ __ of Jesus Christ,
. . to __ __ __ __ __ him to the end . . . shall be
received by baptism into his church."

#13   Missionary:

I Will Share the Gospel of Jesus Christ

Search & Ponder Challenge:
Read D&C, Section 4

D&C 4:2

"Therefore, O ye that embark in the

_ _ _ _ _ _ _ _ of God, see that ye

_ _ _ _ _ _ _ him with all your _ _ _ _ _ _,

might, _ _ _ _ _ and

_ _ _ _ _ _ _ _ _, that ye may stand

blameless before God at the _ _ _ _ day."

#14   Hymns:

The Sacred Hymns Bring Us Blessings

Search & Ponder Challenge:
Read D&C, Section 25

D&C 25:15

"For my _ _ _ _ _ delighteth in the

_ _ _ _ _ of the _ _ _ _ _; yea, the song

of the righteous is a _ _ _ _ _ _ _ unto me,

and it shall be answered with a

_ _ _ _ _ _ _ _ _ upon their heads."

#15   Revelation:

The Prophet Speaks and I Listen

Search & Ponder Challenge:
Read D&C 43:1-7

D&C 43:7

"For verily I say unto you, that he that is

___ ___ ___ ___ ___ ___ ___ ___ ___ of me shall come in at the

___ ___ ___ ___ and be ordained as I have told you

before, to ___ ___ ___ ___ ___ those revelations which

you have received and shall receive through him

whom I have ___ ___ ___ ___ ___ ___ ___ ___ ___."

#16   Love and Unity:

I Will Love and Help Others

Search & Ponder Challenge:
D&C 38:24, 31-31

D&C 38:24

"And let every man ___ ___ ___ ___ ___ ___

his brother as ___ ___ ___ ___ ___ ___ ___,

and practise ___ ___ ___ ___ ___ ___ and

holiness before me."

#17   Bishops:
I Will Support My Church Leaders

Search & Ponder Challenge:
Read D&C 41:9-11

D&C 41:9, 11

"I have called my servant Edward Partridge; and I give a commandment, that he should be appointed by the voice of the church, and __ __ __ __ __ __ __ __ a __ __ __ __ __ __ unto the church . . . And this because his __ __ __ __ __ is __ __ __ __ before me . . ."

#18   Law of Consecration:
I Will Share to Build Up the Kingdom of God

Search & Ponder Challenge:
Read D&C 42:34-39

D&C 42:38

"For inasmuch as ye __ __ it unto the __ __ __ __ __ __ of these, ye __ __ it unto me."

#19   Gifts of the Spirit:

I Can Recognize and Seek True Gifts

Search & Ponder Challenge:
Read D&C 46:11-14, 17-26

D&C 46:11, 14

"For all have not every __ __ __ __ given unto them;

for there are many gifts, and to __ __ __ __ __ man

is given a gift by the __ __ __ __ __ __ of God."

Gift of a Testimony:

"To others it is given to believe on their words, that

they also might have eternal life if they continue

__ __ __ __ __ __ __ __."

#20   Scriptures:

I Love to Study the Scriptures

Search & Ponder Challenge:
Read second half of Introductory Note for
the Pearl of Great Price (explains content)

Pearl of Great Price—Moses: 1:1

"The __ __ __ __ __ of God, which he spake

unto Moses at a time when Moses was caught up

into a high mountain, And he saw God face to

face, and he talked with him, and the

__ __ __ __ __ of God was upon Moses . . ."

D&C 26:1

"Let your __ __ __ __ be devoted to studying

the scriptures . . ."

Read the Scriptures!

#21 Forgiveness:

I Will Forgive Others and Find Peace

Search & Ponder Challenge:
Read D&C 64:9-11

D&C 64:9-10

"Ye ought to __ __ __ __ __ __ __ __ one another; for he that forgiveth __ __ __ his brother his __ __ __ __ __ __ __ __ __ __ __ __ standeth condemned before the Lord; for there remaineth in him the __ __ __ __ __ __ __ __ sin. I, the Lord, will __ __ __ __ __ __ __ __ whom I will forgive, but of you it is required to forgive __ __ __ men."

#22 Revelation:

The Prophets Give Latter-day Revelation

Search & Ponder Challenge:
Read D&C 67:4

D&C 67:4

"And now I, the Lord, give unto you a __ __ __ __ __ __ __ __ __ __ of the __ __ __ __ __ __ of these __ __ __ __ __ __ __ __ __ __ __ __ which are lying before you."

#23   Celestial Kingdom:
I Can Live With Heavenly Father Again

Search & Ponder Challenge:
Read D&C 76:11-24

D&C 76:22-23

"And now, after the many testimonies which have been given of him, this is the testimony, last of all, which we give of him: That he
___ ___ ___ ___ ___! For we ___ ___ ___ him, even on the right hand of ___ ___ ___; and we heard the voice bearing record that he is the Only Begotten of the Father."

#24   Word of Wisdom:
I Will Say "No" to Harmful/"Yes" to Healthful

Search & Ponder Challenge:
Read D&C 89:4-14, 18-21

D&C 89:18-21

"And all saints who remember to keep and do these sayings, walking in obedience to the commandments, shall receive ___ ___ ___ ___ ___ in their navel and marrow to their
___ ___ ___ ___ ___; And shall find wisdom and great treasures of knowledge, even
___ ___ ___ ___ ___ ___ treasures; And shall run and not be weary, and shall walk and not faint."

#25   Sacrifice:

Heavenly Father Blesses Me When I Sacrifice

Search & Ponder Challenge:
Read D&C 88:119 and 95:11-12

D&C 88:119-120

"_ _ _ _ _ _ _ _ yourselves; prepare every
needful thing; and establish a house, even a house of
_ _ _ _ _ _ _, a house of
_ _ _ _ _ _ _ _, a house of faith, a house of
learning, a house of _ _ _ _ _, a house of _ _ _ _ _, a house of
God; That your incomings may be in the name of the Lord; that your
_ _ _ _ _ _ _ _ _ may be in the name of the Lord . . ."

#26   Priesthood Keys:

Unlock the Powers of Heaven

Search & Ponder Challenge:
Read D&C 110

D&C 110:11

Keys to Do Missionary Work:
"Moses appeared before us, and committed unto
us the keys of the _ _ _ _ _ _ _ _ _ _
of Israel from the four parts of the earth . . ."

D&C 110:13-16

Keys of Sealing Power—Temple Work:
"Elijah the prophet . . . [was] . . . sent, to turn the _ _ _ _ _ _ _
of the fathers."

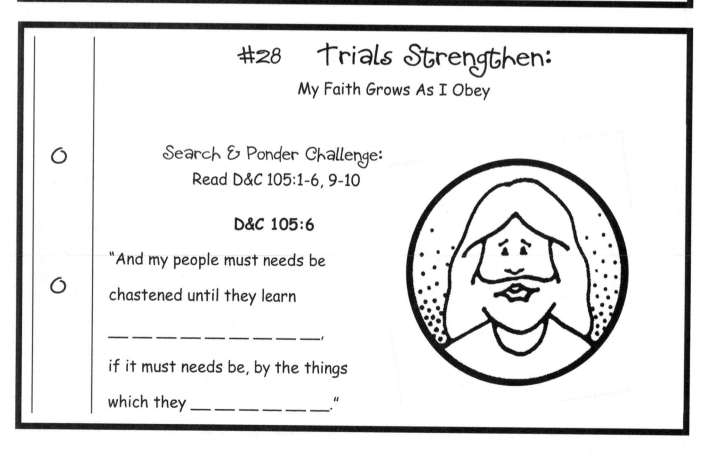

#27   Commandments:
I Will Be Blessed as I Obey and Endure

Search & Ponder Challenge:
Read D&C 82:10

D&C 82:10

"I, the Lord, am __ __ __ __ __ __

when ye __ __ what I say; but

when ye do not what I say, ye

have no __ __ __ __ __ __ __ __."

Commandments bring blessings!

#28   Trials Strengthen:
My Faith Grows As I Obey

Search & Ponder Challenge:
Read D&C 105:1-6, 9-10

D&C 105:6

"And my people must needs be

chastened until they learn

__ __ __ __ __ __ __ __ __ __ __ __,

if it must needs be, by the things

which they __ __ __ __ __ __ __."

#29   Missionary:

I Will Share the Gospel of Jesus Christ

Search & Ponder Challenge:
Read D&C 107:23 and 112:10, 19

D&C 112:10, 19

"Be thou __ __ __ __ __ __; and the Lord thy God shall lead thee by the hand, and give thee answer to thy prayers. ... Wherefore, whithersoever they shall send you, go ye, and I will be with you; and in whatsoever place ye shall __ __ __ __ __ __ __ __ my name an effectual door shall be __ __ __ __ __ __ unto you, that they may receive my word."

#30   Second Coming:

I Will Prepare to Meet My Savior Jesus Christ

Search & Ponder Challenge:
Read D&C 29:10-11 and 107:53-56

D&C 29:10-11

"For the __ __ __ __ is nigh, and that which was spoken by mine apostles must be fulfilled; for as they spoke so shall it come to pass; For I will __ __ __ __ __ __ myself from heaven with power and great glory, with all the hosts thereof, and dwell in righteousness with men on earth a thousand years, and the wicked shall __ __ __ stand."

#31   Prophet Guides:

I Will Listen to the Prophet and Obey

Search & Ponder Challenge:
Read D&C 105:6-10

D&C 105:10

"That they themselves may be

___ ___ ___ ___ ___ ___ ___ ___, and that my people

may be ___ ___ ___ ___ ___ ___ ___ more perfectly,

and have ___ ___ ___ ___ ___ ___ ___ ___ ___ ___ ___, and

___ ___ ___ ___ ___ more perfectly concerning their

___ ___ ___ ___ ___, and the things which I require at

their hands."

#32   Faith:

I Will Rely on Heavenly Father

Search & Ponder Challenge:
Read D&C 121:1-8, 41-46

Doctrine and Covenants 121:7-8

"Peace be unto thy soul; thine adversity and thine

___ ___ ___ ___ ___ ___ ___ ___ ___ ___ ___ shall be but

a small moment; And then, if thou endure it well,

God shall ___ ___ ___ ___ ___ thee on high; thou

shalt triumph over all thy ___ ___ ___ ___."

#33 Pioneer Spirit:

I Will Work Hard to Leave a Legacy of Love

Search & Ponder Challenge:
Read D&C 58:27-28 and 88:124

D&C 88:27-28

"Verily I say, men should be anxiously
_ _ _ _ _ _ _ _ in a good cause,
and do many things of their own free
_ _ _ _ _, and bring to pass much
righteousness; For the _ _ _ _ _ is
in them, wherein they are agents unto themselves. And inasmuch as men do
_ _ _ _ they shall in nowise lose their _ _ _ _ _ _ _."

#34 Baptism for the Dead:

I Can Be Baptized for the Dead

Search & Ponder Challenge:
Read John 3:5, D&C 128:15; 138:29-34

D&C 128:15

"These are principles in relation to the dead and the
living that cannot be lightly passed over, as pertaining
to our _ _ _ _ _ _ _ _ _ _.
For their salvation is necessary and essential to our
salvation, as Paul says concerning the fathers—that
they without us _ _ _ _ _ _ be made
_ _ _ _ _ _ _—neither can we without our
dead be made perfect."

#35   Temples:
I Will Live Worthy to Receive Blessings

Search & Ponder Challenge:
Read D&C 124:26-29, 40-45

D&C 124:40-41

"And verily I say unto you, let this house be built unto my name that I may reveal mine __ __ __ __ __ __ __ __ __ __ therein unto my people. For I deign to reveal unto my church things which have been kept __ __ __ from before the foundation of the world, things that pertain to the dispensation of the fulness of times."

#36   Articles of Faith
Strengthen My Testimony

Search & Ponder Challenge:
Read Articles of Faith in Pearl of Great Price

Articles of Faith 1:13

"We believe in being __ __ __ __ __ __, true, chaste, benevolent, virtuous, and in doing good to all men; indeed, we may say that we __ __ __ __ __ __ the admonition of Paul—We believe all things, we hope all things, we have endured many things, and __ __ __ __ to be able to __ __ __ __ __ __ all things. If there is anything virtuous, lovely, or of __ __ __ __ report or praiseworthy, we __ __ __ __ after these things."

Articles of Faith

#37   Prophet Joseph Smith

Restored the Gospel of Jesus Christ

Search & Ponder Challenge:
Read D&C 135:1-4

D&C 135:3

"Joseph Smith, the __ __ __ __ __ __ __ and
__ __ __ __ __ of the Lord, has done more, save
Jesus only, for the salvation of men in this world,
than any other man that ever lived in it. In the
short space of twenty years, he has brought forth
the Book of Mormon, which he
__ __ __ __ __ __ __ __ __ __ __ by the
__ __ __ __ __ and power of God . . ."

#38   Prophet of Today:

Was Called By God to Lead Us

Search & Ponder Challenge:
Read D&C 112:30-32

Living Prophets

D&C 112:30

"For unto you, the Twelve, and those, the First
__ __ __ __ __ __ __ __ __ __ __ __, who are appointed
with you to be your counselors and your leaders, is the
power of this __ __ __ __ __ __ __ __ __ __ given,
for the last days and for the last time, in which is the
dispensation of the __ __ __ __ __ __ __ of times."

#39   Service:

I Can Be Happy As I Serve

Search & Ponder Challenge:
Read Mosiah 2:17

I love to serve!

Mosiah 2:17
"And behold, I tell you these things that ye may learn __ __ __ __ __ __; that ye may learn that when ye are in the __ __ __ __ __ __ __ of your fellow beings ye are only in the service of your God."

Alma 40:12
"The __ __ __ __ __ __ __ __ of those who are righteous are received into a state of __ __ __ __ __ __ __ __ __ __ . . ."

#40   Pioneers:

I Will Work Hard to Serve Like the Pioneers

Search & Ponder Challenge:
Read D&C 136:1-5, 7, 28-29

D&C 136:2
"Let all the people of the Church of Jesus Christ of Latter-day Saints, and those who journey with them, be __ __ __ __ __ __ __ __ __ __ into companies, with a covenant and promise to keep all the __ __ __ __ __ __ __ __ __ __ __ __ and __ __ __ __ __ __ __ __ __ __ of the Lord our God."

#41   Sabbath Day:
I Will Keep the Sabbath Day Holy

Search & Ponder Challenge:
Read D&C 59:7-19 and 78:19

D&C 59:9-10
"And that thou mayest more fully keep thyself unspotted from the world, thou shalt go to the house of prayer and __ __ __ __ __ up thy sacraments upon my __ __ __ __ day; For verily this is a day appointed unto you to __ __ __ __ from your labors, and to __ __ __ thy devotions unto the Most High."

#42   Faith:
Faith in Jesus Christ Helps with Problems

Search & Ponder Challenge:
Read D&C 8:10 and 20:29

D&C 10:52, 55, 57-58
"And now, behold, according to their __ __ __ __ __ in their __ __ __ __ __ __ __ will I bring this part of my gospel to the knowledge of my people. Behold, I do not bring it to destroy that which they have received, but to build it up. . . . Therefore, whosoever belongeth to my church need not __ __ __ __, for such shall __ __ __ __ __ __ __ the kingdom of heaven. . . . "

Faith in
Jesus Christ

#43   Valiant:

Live Valiantly the Gospel of Jesus Christ

Search & Ponder Challenge:
Read D&C 14:7 and 24:8

D&C 14:7

"And, if you __ __ __ __ __ my

commandments and __ __ __ __ __ __ __

to the end you shall have eternal

__ __ __ __ __, which gift is the greatest

of all the gifts of __ __ __."

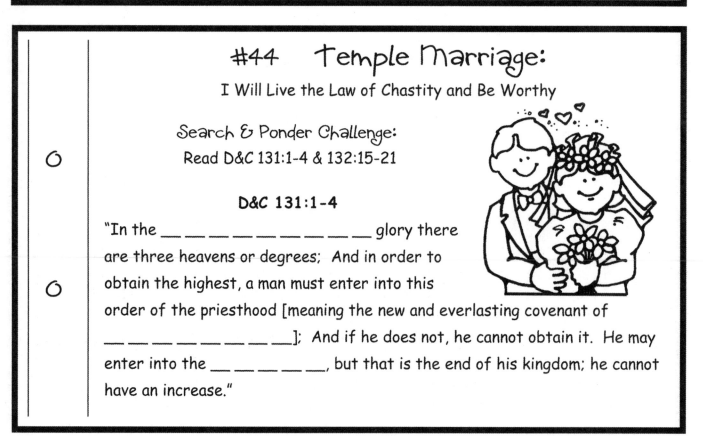

#44   Temple Marriage:

I Will Live the Law of Chastity and Be Worthy

Search & Ponder Challenge:
Read D&C 131:1-4 & 132:15-21

D&C 131:1-4

"In the __ __ __ __ __ __ __ __ __ __ glory there

are three heavens or degrees; And in order to

obtain the highest, a man must enter into this

order of the priesthood [meaning the new and everlasting covenant of

__ __ __ __ __ __ __ __ __]; And if he does not, he cannot obtain it. He may

enter into the __ __ __ __ __, but that is the end of his kingdom; he cannot

have an increase."

#45   Tithing:
Pay a Full Tithing to Build God's Kingdom

Search & Ponder Challenge:
Read Malachi 3:8-12 (Bible)

Malachi 3:10

"Bring ye all the __ __ __ __ __ __ into the storehouse, that there may be meat in mine house, and prove me now herewith, saith the Lord of hosts, if I will not open you the __ __ __ __ __ __ __ of heaven, and pour you out a blessing, that there shall not be room enough to receive it."

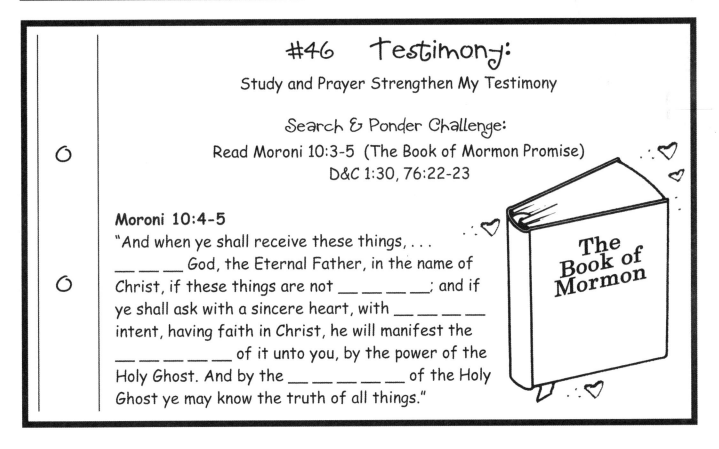

#46   Testimony:
Study and Prayer Strengthen My Testimony

Search & Ponder Challenge:
Read Moroni 10:3-5 (The Book of Mormon Promise)
D&C 1:30, 76:22-23

Moroni 10:4-5
"And when ye shall receive these things, . . . __ __ __ God, the Eternal Father, in the name of Christ, if these things are not __ __ __ __; and if ye shall ask with a sincere heart, with __ __ __ __ intent, having faith in Christ, he will manifest the __ __ __ __ __ of it unto you, by the power of the Holy Ghost. And by the __ __ __ __ __ of the Holy Ghost ye may know the truth of all things."

For Primary, Sharing Time, or Family Home Evening Ideas:
The following books are in full color. Simply tear out, cut out, and enjoy games and activities to motivate gospel learning. Also available for each is a CD-ROM to print the images.

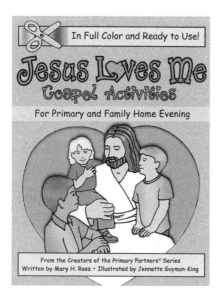

Jesus Loves Me—Gospel Activities:
• Following Jesus' Light • Jesus Blesses Me with His Teachings • Jesus Restored His Church
• Jesus Saved Me from Physical and Spiritual Death
• Jesus Showed His Love • Heavenly Father Promised to Send Jesus • Honoring Jesus
• My Faith Increases As I Learn about Jesus
• The Sacrament Helps Me Remember Jesus' Love

Fun in a Flash! Gospel Activities:
• Accountability • Choose the Right
• Commandments • Faith • Follow Jesus
• The Holy Ghost • Missionary Talents
• Missionary Work • Repentance
• Second Coming • Service • Testimony

Gospel Fun Activities:
• Blessings of the Temple • Consequences
• Family History • Follow the Examples of Jesus
• Happy Family • Invite the Spirit
• Jesus Will Come Again • My Body Is a Temple
• Preparing for the Temple and a Mission
• Prophets • Sabbath Day • Stand as a Witness

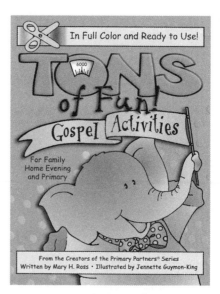

Tons of Fun! Gospel Activities:
• Bless My Family • Child of God
• Choose the Right • Following Jesus
• Following the Prophet
• Gifts to Jesus • Gospel Standards
• Listen and Obey • Repentance
• Responsible Family • Temple Blessings